# A Primer on CO$_2$ and Climate
## Second Edition

Howard C. Hayden

Library of Congress Control Number: 2008926445


Hayden, Howard C.
*A Primer on CO$_2$ and Climate* (2$^{nd}$ Edition)
Howard C. Hayden, Editor
Includes bibliographic references

ISBN    10-digit: 0-9714845-5-4
        13-digit: 978-0-9714845-6-6

Cover design by Daret L. Jones

*Vales Lake Publishing, LLC*
P.O. Box 7609
Pueblo West, CO 81007-0609
SAN: 2 5 4 - 2 5 3

# Table of Contents

# Preliminaries

Carbon dioxide ($CO_2$) is a naturally occurring gas without which the entire biosphere would die.[1]  The reason is that sunlight, acting on chlorophyll in plants, extracts the carbon from atmospheric $CO_2$ and causes plant growth.  Without plants, all animal life dies.

The photosynthetic process releases oxygen ($O_2$) from the $CO_2$ into the atmosphere.  We inhale $O_2$ from the atmosphere, and our blood carries the oxygen around our bodies where it combines with carbon (slowly "burning") to produce $CO_2$.  The blood carries the $CO_2$ to the lungs, where it is exhaled.

The description above is highly simplified, but it drives home the point that $CO_2$ is a necessary part of the biosphere.  Plants absorb $CO_2$ from the air and emit $O_2$.  The animal world eats food, inhales $O_2$, and exhales $CO_2$. The whole process is *recycling*, pure and simple.

The whole flap about $CO_2$ is that combustion of fuels also produces $CO_2$, and that a buildup of $CO_2$ in the atmosphere will lead to catastrophic warming because of the greenhouse effect.  Actually, there are several main questions, to wit:

- Is the earth warming?
- If the earth is warming, is mankind responsible?
- If the earth is warming, is that a bad situation?
- If the earth is warming, and if mankind's use of fossil fuels is responsible, and if the situation is bad, is there anything we can do to remedy the situation?

## The Greenhouse Phenomenon

In the standard — but incorrect — view, sunlight enters a greenhouse through glass, which is transparent.  The interior of the greenhouse radiates heat away, but the radiation is in the infrared (IR), to which the glass is opaque; therefore the heat remains in the greenhouse.

Incorrect statements are often given by weathercasters who refer to "radiational cooling" that, according to their implications, exists on clear nights and does not exist on cloudy nights.  The clouds do not inhibit the ground from radiating IR; the ground radiates all the time, day and night, clear or cloudy, in a manner that depends only upon its temperature.  The

---

[1] We exclude such exotic things as tubeworms living at undersea volcanic vents.

clouds absorb and scatter IR, and they emit IR according to the clouds' temperatures. Some of that IR radiates toward the earth and serves as a source of heat. The clouds exhibit a greenhouse effect.

In an oversimplified (and likely incorrect) view (see "A Final Note," page 69), sunlight reaches the earth's surface through the transparent atmosphere. The surface of the earth radiates heat away, but the radiation is absorbed by *greenhouse gases* (GHGs, *one* of which is $CO_2$), thereby retaining the heat. There is certainly an *atmospheric* effect that retains heat, but it is a mistake to attribute everything to GHGs. For example, water *droplets* in clouds exhibit a greenhouse effect, and would do so even if water *vapor* ($H_2O$ molecules in the air, or "gaseous water") did not absorb IR at all.

$CO_2$ absorbs *some* of the IR, but by no means all of it. The same can be said of the other greenhouse gases: $H_2O$, $CH_4$ (methane, the major component of natural gas), $O_3$ (ozone), and a few other trace gases. $H_2O$ molecules can easily form dimers (pairs of $H_2O$ molecules, making $H_4O_2$) and trimers (triplets), which also absorb IR, but have different spectral characteristics from $H_2O$.

The most important greenhouse gas is water vapor, partly because it is more abundant (about 100 times as abundant as $CO_2$), and partly because the $H_2O$ molecule, its dimers, and trimers etc. have many ways to absorb IR. But adding a little more $H_2O$ to the atmosphere does little to add to the greenhouse effect because all of the radiation that $H_2O$ can absorb is already being absorbed.

Incoming sunlight has a large proportion of infrared — *near* infrared — and that radiation is strongly absorbed by $H_2O$ and $CO_2$, thereby heating the atmosphere. The range of wavelengths of importance is from approximately 700 nanometers (nm, billionths of a meter) to perhaps 2,500 nm.

The earth (ground, oceans, ice, snow, etc.) emits infrared, but all of it is in the *far* infrared region, roughly 5,000 nm to 30,000 nm (5 micrometers to 30 micrometers). In this wavelength range, $H_2O$ absorbs over a far wider range of wavelengths than $CO_2$ does. For either gas, as the concentration increases, each increment in concentration produces less greenhouse effect than the previous; when radiation has been absorbed, it is not present to be absorbed further.

## A Frightening Graph

Let us begin by looking at the carbon dioxide concentration, as shown in Fig. 1. The data in the graph are correct [1, 2], and the graph looks very impressive. Since I am not Al Gore, I'll tell you what is wrong with it.

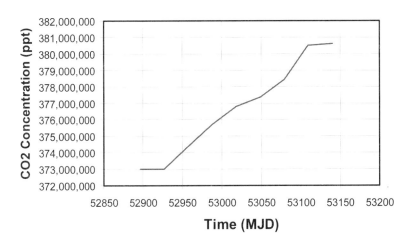

# CO2 Concentration (Mauna Loa)

**Figure 1: Carbon dioxide concentration versus time, shown in Gee-Whiz fashion.**

You will notice that the horizontal axis is time, expressed in MJD, with which you may not be familiar. That's Modified Julian Day, a reckoning used by astronomers. The graph covers only the period from September 2004 to May 2005, through the northern-hemisphere mid-fall to mid-spring, while northern hemisphere plants are dormant. Such a short period says absolutely nothing about long-term trends. I won't bother showing a Gee-Whiz graph of $CO_2$ *decreasing* over a short spring-to-fall period corresponding to Fig. 1. (The term *Gee-Whiz Graph* comes from Darrell Huff's timeless book, *How to Lie with Statistics*)

The second thing wrong with the Fig. 1 is that the vertical axis does not start at zero. Despite the dramatic appearance of the graph, it represents only a 2-percent change in carbon dioxide concentration.

The third thing wrong with the graph is the huge numbers on the vertical axis. The number 380,000,000 might scare the pants off Count Dracula, but what it refers to is ppt, parts per *trillion*. In every trillion units of atmosphere, there are 380 million parts that are $CO_2$. Let's express that a different way. It means that 0.038 percent of the atmosphere is $CO_2$. That's about a twenty-fifth of one percent, equivalent to 4 cents out of 100 dollars.

# Carbon Dioxide in the Past

Sometimes carbon dioxide concentration increases. Sometimes it decreases. It all depends on the time scale.

The most commonly shown graph of $CO_2$ concentration versus time (Fig. 2) is one representing data taken by Keeling at Mauna Loa, Hawaii, out in the middle of the Pacific Ocean, undisturbed by local factories or high traffic. Like Fig. 1, the zero of the vertical axis is suppressed, the time period is short, and the $CO_2$ concentration is given in big numbers. (A friend attending a talk overheard some uneducated folks in front of him comment that "Hey, those numbers are *big*. That's a lot of stuff!")

Scientists work with graphs like Fig. 2 without any confusion, because experience has taught them the implications of those representations of data. On the other hand, Al Gore deliberately panders to ignorance (Fig. 3, from *An Inconvenient Truth*) by showing the data with no scale whatsoever, and displayed alongside a picture of the earth to make it look dramatic.

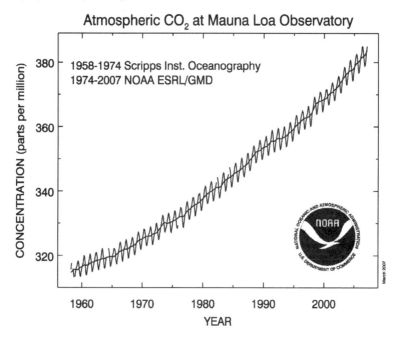

Figure 2: Atmospheric $CO_2$ measured at Mauna Loa [1]. It suffers from the same Gee-Whiz maladies as Fig. 1, though at least the time scale covers more than one season, and the $CO_2$ numbers are not in the millions.

Primer on $CO_2$ and Climate

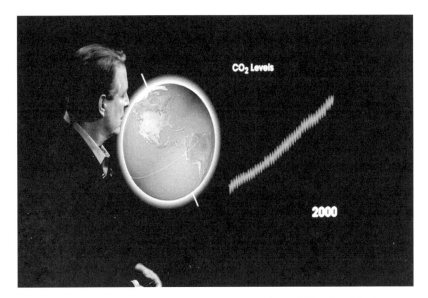

**Figure 3: Al Gore's Gee-Whiz representation of Fig. 2, with the whole earth alongside for comparison.**

Now let us put this together and show the Mauna Loa data without any Gee-Whiz artifacts. Figure 4 shows the results. Yes, in the time span since the late 1950s, atmospheric $CO_2$ has been increasing. Yes, there are seasonal variations. No, $CO_2$ is not a major part of the atmosphere.

Since it is the habit of scientists to work with graphs like Fig. 2, and with the understanding that 400 parts per million represents one twenty-fifth of one percent (0.04%), I will not bother modifying published graphs to translate them into percentage. I will simply present other graphs from the scientific literature showing past $CO_2$ concentrations, usually in ppm. For all graphs, look at the scales to see whether the zero is suppressed.

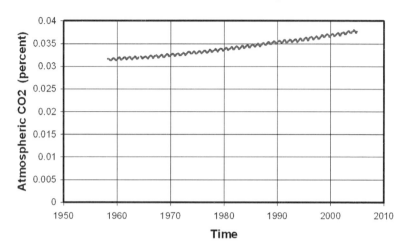

**Figure 4:** Atmospheric carbon dioxide from Mauna Loa measurements with no Gee-Whiz artifacts. Since 1958, $CO_2$ concentration measured at Mauna Loa has increased from 0.032 percent to 0.038 percent of the atmosphere.

Let's look at a longer time scale. Figure 5 shows $CO_2$ concentration measured in ice cores at the Vostok research station in Antarctica [graph from ref 3, constructed from data at ref. 4], thousands of miles from tropical Hawaii. The time scale extends back 400,000 years. Excluding the present, the concentration has varied from 0.018% of the atmosphere to 0.03%. Except for the short periods when $CO_2$ concentration has been high, all of that long time span has been characterized by ice ages.

In Fig. 5 (from ref. [3]), the last 10,000 years (the most recent interglacial) are squeezed into the area to the right of the last tick mark on the time axis, and the industrial era is too narrow to show up. Notice that the $CO_2$ concentration is given in *ppmv* which means parts per million by *volume* (as opposed to *weight*), and "by volume" is actually what is meant by all data in this book.

You may well be scratching your head wondering where that $CO_2$ came from when concentration was rising, and where it went when concentration was falling. Suffice it for the present to say that the increases were not caused by SUVs and coal-fired power plants, and the decreases were not caused by regulations issued in Washington, D.C.

6             Primer on $CO_2$ and Climate

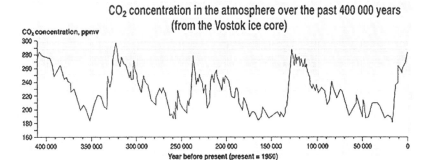

CO₂ concentration in the atmosphere over the past 400 000 years (from the Vostok ice core)

**Figure 5:** $CO_2$ concentration for the last 400,000 years, as determined from ice cores at Vostok in Antarctica. The temperature data will be discussed shortly.

Sometimes, you will see Fig. 5 shown with a dramatic vertical line representing an extremely sharp increase during the present fossil-burning era. Al Gore shows this Gee-Whiz feature (see Fig. 6, from *An Inconvenient Truth*) by standing on an elevated platform to dramatize how high $CO_2$ levels will be in 50 years — on his zero-suppressed graph scales — by calculations that according to him are universally agreed upon.

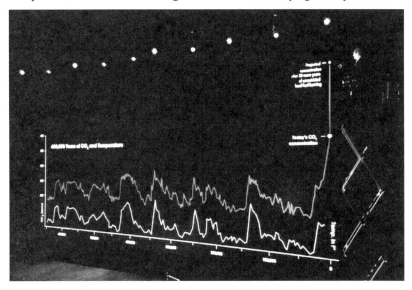

**Figure 6:** Al Gore standing on an elevated platform to dramatize projected high $CO_2$ concentrations in 50 years.

During the last 400,000 years, there could be literally hundreds of similar rapid increases, but the nature of the data and the nature of the analysis — the data are recorded at about 1000-year intervals — would prohibit them from showing up as sharp increases.

There is another reason why the abrupt rise is a mere artifact. It all has to do with the three most important aspects of real estate: Location, Location, Location. Hawaii is not Antarctica. Antarctica is not Hawaii.

Much is often made of the fact that we are now experiencing the highest $CO_2$ concentration in the last 400,000 years. Al Gore makes a point of the fact that in the entire 400,000 years, $CO_2$ concentration has never (before very recently) exceeded 300 parts per million. (A detailed look at the numbers from *Vostok* does show that the highest concentration in the ice core was just a tiny bit under 300 ppm.) But those aren't the only measurements ever made by anybody.

## CO2 Concentration

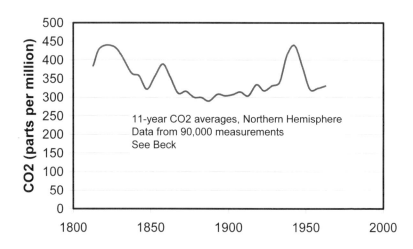

**Figure 7:** **$CO_2$ measurements made by chemical means in the Northern Hemisphere, 1812-1964, 11-year averages of 90,000 measurements. [From Beck, 5]**

Figure 7 shows results of 90,000 measurements made during the period 1812 to 1964 by accurate chemical means, mostly to an accuracy of ± 10 ppm [5]. Most of the readings *exceed* 300 parts per million, and some are above 400 ppm. Beck [5] points out that Keeling, who measured $CO_2$ at Mauna Loa, merely dismissed all data inconsistent with his own. But

Keeling is not alone. In a very recent *Scientific American* article [6], Collins *et al* say, "The atmospheric concentrations of carbon dioxide, methane and nitrous oxide remained roughly stable for nearly 10,000 years, before the abrupt and rapidly accelerating increases of the past 200 years."

We will return to this topic later after discussing $CO_2$ sources and sinks. Suffice it to say now that the $CO_2$ record from Antarctica may not necessarily be representative of the $CO_2$ record in tropical Hawaii, and that readings taken in the Northern Hemisphere exceeded 400 ppm in the early 1800s.

Now we will look further back in time, at the phanerozoic record. (The term basically refers to the time during which life has existed on earth.) Figure 8 [from ref. 7, 8] shows a much longer time scale that extends back about 1500 times as far as the scale in Fig. 5. Note that the time scale is backwards, with the past to the right and the present to the left. The 400,000-year span of Fig. 5 is a tiny sliver on the left.

One thing to notice in Fig. 8 is that the present $CO_2$ concentration is indeed anomalous. *During the last half-billion years, $CO_2$ concentration has never been as low as it is now.* Yes, LOW.

Another thing to notice in Fig. 8 is the lettering at the bottom, which is geologists' shorthand for various eras. For example, *J* represents the Jurassic, the time of dinosaurs. During that long time span, $CO_2$ concentration was approximately 10 times as high (some readings show 25 times as high) as now. It was an extraordinarily productive time. All of those huge creatures were supported, directly or indirectly, by vegetation that thrived in the high-$CO_2$ environment. (Yes, $CO_2$ — a naturally occurring gas that the benighted Supreme Court says should be "regulated" by the EPA — is plant food.)

"Carbon dioxide gas must be introduced into greenhouses to maintain plant growth, as even in vented greenhouses the concentration of carbon dioxide can fall during daylight hours to as low as 200 ppm, at which level photosynthesis is significantly retarded. Venting can help offset the drop in carbon dioxide, but will never raise it back to ambient levels of 340 ppm. Carbon dioxide supplementation is the only known method to overcome this deficiency. Direct introduction of pure carbon dioxide is ideal, but rarely done because of cost constraints. Most greenhouses burn methane or propane to supply the additional $CO_2$, ..." [9]

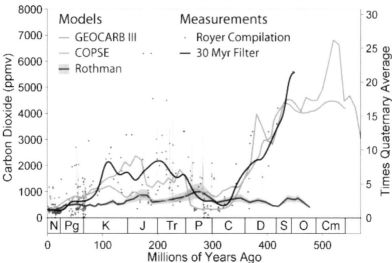

**Figure 8: Carbon dioxide concentrations for the last 600 million years, expressed in parts per million (left) and multiples of current concentration (right). The last 400,000-year period of Fig. 5 is squeezed into a very thin sliver on the left. Dots represent data, and lines represent various models. The right-hand scale expresses $CO_2$ levels as a multiple of today's concentration. [8]**

To dramatize the high levels of $CO_2$ in the Jurassic, Gore would have to be hanging from a very high crane outside the building, somewhat as shown in Fig. 9.

Global warming alarmists use expressions like "turning point", "tipping point", "before it's too late", "we are facing a catastrophe", "trigger point", and "the looming (fill in your own word) crisis", to name a few, to describe the near future. Perhaps it's time to cool the rhetoric. Jurassic $CO_2$ levels that were up to twenty-five times as high as current ones did not lead to catastrophic global warming, and there's no credible reason to believe that we are headed to catastrophe.

The age of dinosaurs ended, but not because of high $CO_2$ concentration. It now seems pretty certain that the Jurassic ended with the crash of a meteorite into the Gulf of Mexico.

The cause of the earlier Permian extinction — which was much greater — is not so certain. Atmospheric *oxygen* plummeted at the time, but $CO_2$ concentration held pretty steady.

It should be humbling to note that Permian rock is yellowish everywhere in the world, and that post-Permian rock is reddish, and continues that way for some 50 million years. Anything that humans can do is utterly puny by comparison.

## The Temperature Record

Just like $CO_2$ concentration, temperature increases and temperature decreases. It all depends on the time scale.

But let us begin with some fundamentals. There is no such thing as *the* temperature of the earth. Moreover, the *average* temperature is basically meaningless, as useful as the average of numbers in the phone book. However,

CO$_2$ level in the Jurassic

Figure 9: Al Gore and T-Rex look at Jurassic $CO_2$. The dark box at the bottom is Fig. 6 reduced to fit.

average temperature *changes* are *sometimes* meaningful.

Why is the average temperature meaningless? Let's imagine a single room where the average temperature is 20 °C (68 °F). That average can be achieved by a thermostat that holds the temperature nearly constant, or by having the windows wide open while the temperature ranges between 0 °C (32 °F) and 40 °C (104 °F). For another example, consider that the numerical average of two temperatures, one of boiling water and one of water at the ice temperature (0 C) is 50 °C (122 °F), but a teaspoon of boiling water poured into a cold lake will raise the temperature by an utterly immeasurable amount.

Or on a spatial scale, if every place in Texas has the same temperature (20 °C, for example), the weather is calm. If the temperature is 40 °C (104 °F) in Waco and 0 °C (32 °F) along the Gulf Coast (with similar readings throughout the state so that the average is 20 °C), there will be violent weather, because the temperature *gradient* drives the winds.

Now, how does one calculate the average temperature of (say) Utah? Take the average of 10,000 thermometer readings around Salt Lake City and 3 readings in Moab? Decide that the average readings of 10,000 thermometers represents (say) 200 square kilometers around Salt Lake City and that the average readings of the three thermometers represents 200 square kilometers around Moab? A statistician may figure out a good method *in principle*, but not *in practice*, because so many areas are uninhabited. Furthermore, a thermodynamicist can easily prove that there is no unique average temperature and that the concept is meaningless.

We are actually interested in whether the earth is warming. As one knows from looking at an array of thermometers in hardware stores, although they may disagree by a few degrees they can still correctly reflect a *change* of 1 degree. In other words, it is perfectly possible to record *changes* in temperature — the temperature *anomaly* — without being able to measure temperature accurately. Still, finding *average temperature changes* is fraught with the same difficulties as measuring the average temperature.

The latest IPCC report (ref 10, in the "Frequently Asked Questions" chapter) shows a temperature history in which there are several slopes (rates of warming). The long-term trend has the lowest slope, and as the time interval gets smaller, the slope gets larger. The obvious purpose of the gimmick is to convince the naive reader that the rate of warming is increasing. It is a matter of statistics that short-term trends can always be chosen that are steeper than long-term trends of the same data set. What the IPCC does not do is choose a (say) 25-year interval that shows a temperature decline, as one could equally logically do.

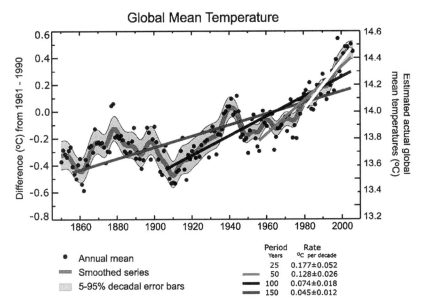

Global Mean Temperature

| | Period<br>Years | Rate<br>°C per decade |
|---|---|---|
| • Annual mean | 25 | 0.177±0.052 |
| Smoothed series | 50 | 0.128±0.026 |
| 5-95% decadal error bars | 100 | 0.074±0.018 |
| | 150 | 0.045±0.012 |

**Figure 10: The temperature record of the world, as shown in the latest (2007) IPCC report [10]. Data points are dots, gray shading represents margin of error, and lines show a family of increasing rates of warming. The purpose is obviously to frighten rather than to inform.**

Satellites fly around the earth in many orbits and take readings of temperature using *microwave sounding units* (MSUs). They perform *uniform* sampling, rather than the haphazard sampling of earth-based thermometers, and take the average using equal weighting for equal areas. They can also distinguish between the lower troposphere (where we live) and the upper troposphere. From a statistical viewpoint, the satellite technique is vastly superior to using readings from thermometers placed here and there around the globe, primarily where people live and provide artificial heat. The data are updated monthly at the University of Alabama Huntsville website [11].

# Satellite Temperature Anomaly

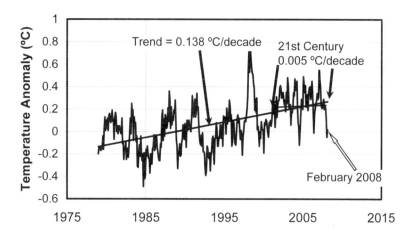

**Figure 11:** The average temperature anomaly of the earth as reckoned by satellite, December 1978 to February 2008. The trend for the entire period is 0.138 °C per decade. Since about 2001, the world-wide average temperature has remained essentially constant, with a trend of 0.005 °C per decade.

On the other hand, the satellite data extend back only to December, 1978, not even as far back as the Mauna Loa record for $CO_2$ extends, making long-term trend estimates impossible. Figure 11 shows the average temperature anomaly (change) since the satellites were put into orbit. Given the spread of the data, you might think you could write your name through the data points. A mathematical technique called *least-squares fitting* allows us to determine the "trend" — a figure that is good only for the time interval of the actual data, and of no value for predicting the future — of 0.138 °C per decade.

Since about 2001, the temperature has remained essentially constant, but there is no reason to believe that the trend will continue. Perhaps warming will continue; perhaps there will be a cooling period.

It is a fool's game to project very far into the future, but we are free to look at the past. What is the temperature record dating farther into the past? The thermometer was invented in 1612, but it took a couple of centuries before they were widespread enough to cover more than a tiny fraction of the earth. To put the timing in context, it was three centuries after that invention that New Mexico and Arizona became states. That is, the mere invention of the thermometer did not lead immediately to thermometers all around the globe.

Figure 12 shows the temperature anomaly from 1880 to the present, as compiled by NOAA. Official land-based air temperatures are determined by thermometers in specially designed white louvered boxes. Oceanic temperatures are measured by seagoing vessels, but no standard of measurement elevation (for air) or measurement depth (for water) seems to have existed. Be assured that huge areas of the world went unmeasured for a long time.

The temperature generally decreased until about 1910; it rose during the next three decades, cooled and remained nearly constant for four decades, and has risen for about 25 years. World War II ended in 1945, and the post-war boom began. The boom was fueled by coal and petroleum, of course. Figure 12 shows temperature rising from 1975 to 2005 (0.55 °C in 30 years), but the rate of rise is not appreciably different from that of the 1910-1940 period (0.46 °C in 30 years). If extrapolations were made from any of the earlier trends, they would be wildly wrong today.

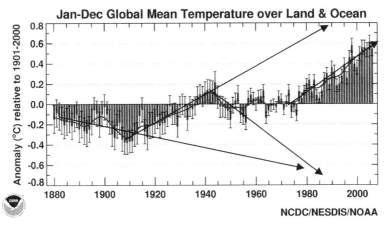

Figure 12: Global Mean Temperature anomaly from 1880 to present, compiled from land-based records and ships' logs as well, from NOAA [12]. The arrows represent extrapolations that might have appeared reasonable at the time, but which would be wildly wrong today. Compare these "trends" with those of Fig. 10, which show nothing but increasing slopes and those of Fig. 11, which has one trend dating back to December 1978, and another dating back to January, 2001.

Now let us look further back in history, determining temperature when no thermometers existed. There exist various proxies for temperature, usually with one fault or another. For example, tree-rings may be wider because the climate is warmer, there is more water, there is more carbon dioxide (or other nutrients) or fewer insects. Glaciers can grow because it is colder or because there is more snow. They can recede because it is warmer or because less snow falls. Grain harvests (for which records extend back for centuries in some cases) are subject not only to temperature but to cloudiness, drought, rains during harvest season, and insect populations. Quite apart from that, warming or cooling in one area of the globe is not necessarily correlated with warming or cooling of the earth as a whole.

There are some indicators, however, that speak directly to temperature. For example, plants can usually tolerate much warmer temperatures than exist in their optimum environment, but colder temperatures are not tolerated. Birch trees prosper in warmer climates, oaks in cooler, and pines in colder yet. Their pollen records their history. Trees grow up to tree line, and no further. Trees grow just so far into the arctic, but no further. One useful measure from past cultures is the length of the growing season.

One display of past temperature is the now infamous "hockey stick" graph (Fig. 13, from ref. [13]). Derived almost exclusively from tree-ring data, it displays reconstructed temperature for the last 1000 years. It caused quite a ruckus when it was published. It showed nearly constant (slightly descending) temperature from 1000 about 1900, followed by a dramatic rise to the present, thereby denying the existence of the Medieval Warm Period, and downplaying the Little Ice Age.

The first skeptics to question the "hockey stick" graph were economists, McKitrick and McIntire [14]. If that sounds strange, it is useful to note that Mann *et al* applied a statistical technique well known in the economics community. Economists have seen dozens of hockey stick graphs representing stock prices and lots of other economic parameters, all such graphs coming from people who did not understand that the procedure routinely leads to hockey sticks when applied incorrectly. To make a long story short, Congress asked a team of statisticians to investigate the matter. The team found that the graph was indeed a result of poor statistical procedures. [15]

Though the hockey stick graph figured prominently in the previous report of the Inter*governmental* Panel on Climate Change (IPCC Third Assessment Report "AR3", ref. 10) and in much of the global-warming frenzy that it caused, the latest IPCC report (*Fourth Assessment Report,* "AR4," 2007) makes no reference to it. That is, even the highly political IPCC has abandoned the hockey stick.

**Departures in temperature in °C (from the 1961-1990 average)**

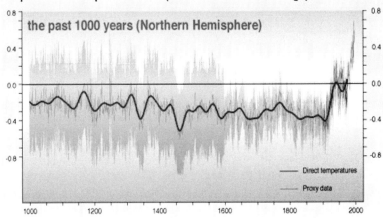

Figure 13: The infamous "hockey stick" graph of Mann and colleagues. It contradicted long-accepted data about global temperature, including the Medieval Warm Period. This graph has been thoroughly discredited by statisticians.

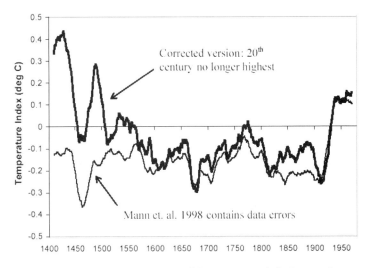

Figure 14: Temperature record with correct statistical procedures (upper) and the hockey stick analysis (lower), both applied to the data set provided by Mann.

McKitrick and McIntire applied proper statistics to the data supplied by Mann with the result shown in Fig. 14. The most prominent change is the restoration of the Medieval Warm Period, as it has long been known to geologists and others. Before we go further, note that the time axis stops a bit short of the year 2000 (as it must for the given kind of analysis). Allowing for a decade from the end of the graph to the present, one might add about 0.14 °C, which would still make the present about 0.2 °C below the Medieval Warm Period.

Mann has claimed that the Medieval Warm Period (MWP) was a local phenomenon — so what if the Vikings settled southern Greenland during that time? — so it is useful to look beyond the graphs to raw data. Figure 15 shows photographs of a 1000-year old foxtail pine above the present tree line in Sequoia National Park, and a 5000-year old spruce (well beyond Mann's 1000-year time period) from the Canadian Arctic. That the trees could have lived there at those times indicates that those two regions were warmer than they are now.

Figure 15: Left. A foxtail pine from above tree-line in the Bighorn Plateau of Sequoia National Park, from 1000 years ago. Right: a 5000-year old spruce in the Canadian Arctic.

But there are many other sources of data from around the world attesting to the existence of the MWP. For example, Peruvian pollen, sailors' reports from Argentina, and stalagmites from South Africa all show evidence that the MWP was not confined to Europe and Greenland [16].

In *An Inconvenient Truth* (see Fig. 16), Al Gore sneers at the idea of a medieval warm period (MWP), using the thoroughly discredited hockey stick graph. Since the MWP doesn't show up on his graph, it must not exist. Soon after the hockey stick appeared in print, it might have been just a mistake to accept the hockey stick at face value, at least for somebody unacquainted with geological history. By the time Gore produced *An Inconvenient Truth*, however, the facts were known, and acceptance of the hockey stick could hardly be attributed to mere ignorance.

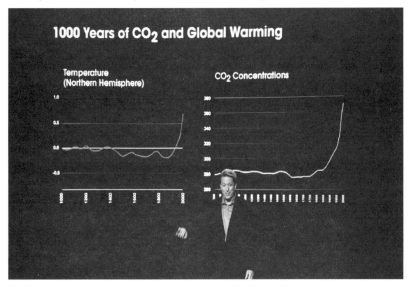

Figure 16:  Al Gore using the hockey-stick graph in *An Inconvenient Truth*.

On a longer time scale, Figure 17 shows the temperature anomaly since the last ice age, a time when mile-high glaciers covered New England, and moving glaciers gouged grooves in rock visible today in New York City's Central Park. Of interest are three warm periods, starting with the Holocene Climate Optimum (ca. 8000 years ago to 4000 years ago), as it has been called by generations of geologists. After a 2000-year cold period came the Roman Warm Period centered at about 1800 years ago, and the Medieval Warm Period (centered about 800 years ago). The warm periods were not caused by "energy wastrels," "addiction to oil," or jet-setters who failed to buy carbon credits.

To determine temperatures existing in the deep past, the common method is to measure concentrations of the rare isotope — $^{18}O$ (alternatively written $O^{18}$ and O-18), which comprises 0.2% of natural oxygen. Oxygen-18 is heavier than the normal oxygen-16, and perforce, so are water molecules containing oxygen-18. Accordingly, and with mathematical predictability, these heavier water molecules evaporate less readily than regular water, and the effect is more pronounced at lower temperature. The most common usage of this argument is applied to water vapor.

Imagine some water vapor from the ocean that encounters cold air. Suppose that the air mass is heading toward the interior of Antarctica. Water droplets form (possibly as snow), and they will preferentially contain a higher concentration of O-18 than the remaining vapor. As the precipitation falls, the vapor continues to move to a place where it is colder yet and more condensation and more precipitation can occur. This precipitation is formed from O-18-depleted vapor, so it is lower in O-18 concentration than the earlier precipitation.

Now if the air is generally warmer, the drop-off of O-18 concentration is slower, so that in (relatively) warm times in Antarctic, the snow falling in the interior is richer in O-18 than it is in colder times.

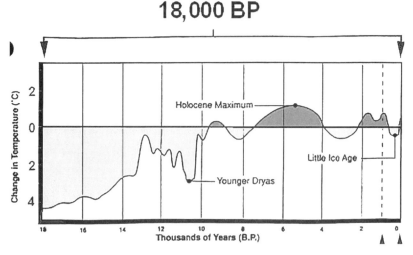

Figure 17: The temperature anomaly for the last 18,000 years (figure adapted from ref. [17]).

Investigators measure a quantity called $\delta O^{18}$ ("delta O-18") the difference between O-18 concentration at the time and O-18 concentration of a standard called the Vienna Standard Mean Ocean Water (VSMOW).

Accordingly, some paleo-temperature records use $\delta O^{18}$ as a proxy for temperature. It is common to see $\delta O^{18}$ plotted vertically on one side of a graph, and the inferred temperature (or sometimes temperature anomaly) on the other side. Figure 18 shows the interpreted temperature anomaly in degrees Celsius, but $\delta O^{18}$ was the quantity directly measured.

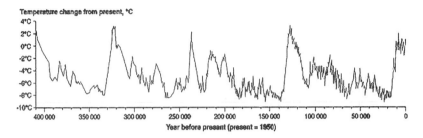

Figure 18: The temperature anomaly in the Vostok (Antarctica) ice cores, as determined from $\delta O^{18}$ from UNEP [3]

Figure 18 shows the temperature anomaly of the earth for the last 400,000 years, as determined by $\delta O^{18}$ measurements. Notice that the majority of the time, the earth has been locked in 100,000-year ice ages with brief (10,000-year) interglacial periods.

It is tempting to look at Figures 5 and 18, see a correlation, and regard the correlation as proof that high $CO_2$ causes high temperature. For example, Al Gore says, "There is one relationship that is more powerful than all the others, and it is this: when there is more carbon dioxide, the temperature gets warmer." I recommend that the reader not jump to hasty conclusions.

In fact, Fig. 18 shows the atmospheric effect on warming, but not in the way Al Gore says. We discuss that matter on page 29.

# Carbon Dioxide Sources and Sinks

Our bodily energy comes from slow combustion of the food we eat. Thus, we inhale oxygen and exhale carbon dioxide. Plants use sunlight to convert carbon dioxide into carbon (retained) and oxygen (emitted).

That is, carbon dioxide is a perfectly natural — and *necessary* — part of the cycle of life, in spite of recent attempts to have it declared a "pollutant." Figure 19 shows some sources, sinks, and reservoirs of carbon dioxide (the list is incomplete). Tables 1, 2, and 3 [from Bice, 18] present the important numbers from Fig. 19. Importantly, *cold water* absorbs $CO_2$ and *warm water* emits $CO_2$. In some cases, the process is as simple as that of a soda pop emitting its $CO_2$ ("fizz") faster when it is warm; in others it is more complicated (and slow), involving oceanic biochemistry.

Before we go further, let us understand something about the quantities in Fig. 19. All of the numbers are rough estimates, save one. We have good worldwide records of coal, oil, and natural gas consumption, and the Energy Information Agency reports that we produced 7.4 billion tonnes of carbon in 2004. (Note that $CO_2$ emissions are often expressed in terms of the mass of the $CO_2$, and just as often in terms of the mass of the carbon itself. The 7.4 billion-tonne figure is the mass of the *carbon* itself, not of carbon dioxide. Multiply carbon mass by $44/12 = 3.667$ to get mass of $CO_2$.)

We have a pretty good idea of how much $CO_2$ is actually in the atmosphere, but not precisely, because the concentration varies with latitude, altitude, and temperature.

From there on, the numbers get more approximate. There is no way to get accurate data on the worldwide removal of $CO_2$ by land-based or marine plants. Other references [19] say that the ocean absorbs 92, not 90, billion tonnes of carbon annually. But certainly, all numbers in the table of Fig. 19 are also variable, to some extent. Higher carbon dioxide concentration causes faster plant growth, for example, as well as faster absorption by cold surface waters. Higher ocean surface temperature causes higher $CO_2$ emissions.

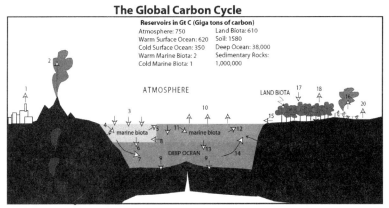

## The Global Carbon Cycle

**Reservoirs in Gt C (Giga tons of carbon)**

Atmosphere: 750    Land Biota: 610
Warm Surface Ocean: 620    Soil: 1580
Cold Surface Ocean: 350    Deep Ocean: 38,000
Warm Marine Biota: 2    Sedimentary Rocks:
Cold Marine Biota: 1    1,000,000

Figure 1. The global carbon cycle, as best estimated, in 1994. Data slightly modified from Siegenthaler and Sarmiento, 1995; Kwon and Schnoor, 199

### Key to Flows:

1) Fossil Fuel Burning — 5 Gt C/yr
2) Volcanic Emissions — 0.6 Gt C/yr
3) Uptake of $CO_2$ by cold surface waters of the oceans — 90 GtC/yr
4) Photosynthesis of marine biota in cold surface waters — 18 GtC/yr
5) Respiration of living marine biota and rapid recycling of dead biota in cold surface waters — 14 GtC/yr
6) Sinking of dead marine biota (both organic and inorganic carbon) from cold water into deep water — 4 GtC/yr
7) Downwelling of cold surface water (mainly near the poles) — 96.2 GtC/yr
8) Advection (horizontal transfer) from warm to cold surface water — 10 Gt C/yr
9) Sedimentation on sea floor (both organic and inorganic carbon) stores carbon in sedimentary rocks — 0.6Gt C/yr
10) Release of $CO_2$ by warm surface waters of the oceans — 90 GtC/yr

11) Photosynthesis of marine biota in warm surface waters — 32 GtC/yr
12) Respiration of living marine biota and rapid recycling of dead biota in warm surface waters — 26 GtC/yr
13) Sinking of dead marine biota (both organic and inorganic carbon) from warm water into deep water — 6 GtC/yr
14) Upwelling of deep water (at equator and along edges of continents) — 105.6 GtC/yr
15) River runoff transfers carbon from the land to the sea — 0.6 Gt C/yr (2/3 to warm ocean, 1/3 cold)
16) Deforestation and land clearing releases $CO2$ into the atmosphere — 1.5 Gt C/yr
17) Photosynthesis of land biota — 110 Gt C/yr
18) Respiration of land biota — 50 Gt C/yr
19) Litter fall and below-ground loss from plant roots transfers carbon to the soil — 60 Gt C/yr
20) Respiration of micoorganisms in the soil releases $CO2$ into the atmosphere — 59.4 Gt C/yr

Figure 19: Drawing: Carbon reservoirs in billion tonnes of carbon, from Bice [18]. Numbers with arrows refer to table. Table: annual flows (billion tons per year). For example, the atmosphere contains 750 billion tonnes (1st listing in drawing), and fossil fuel emissions amount to 5 billion tonnes per year (a bit before 1995). The world produced 7.4 billion tonnes in 2004.

## Table 1:  Some Sources of Atmospheric $CO_2$

| Source | Annual Flow (billion tonnes C/year) |
|---|---|
| Terrestrial plant decay | 60 |
| Warm ocean emissions | 90 |
| Fossil burning | 7.4 (2004) |

## Table 2:  Some Sinks of Atmospheric $CO_2$

| Sink | Annual Flow (billion tonnes C/ year) |
|---|---|
| Terrestrial plant growth | 61 |
| Cold ocean absorption | 90 |

How does a molecule of $CO_2$ become absorbed by the ocean or by terrestrial vegetation?  It's not all that easy for a molecule two miles up in the atmosphere to make contact with anything at ground level.  The most efficient process for returning $CO_2$ to ground level involves precipitation. The surface area presented by untold trillions of water droplets in the air is enormous compared to the surface area of the ocean, and water droplets invariably form only when the temperature is low: below the dew point. The cold droplets absorb $CO_2$ and fall to the land or ocean as somewhat acidified rain.  If conditions are right, the $CO_2$ may be absorbed in photosynthesis or cold water, or be released back to the atmosphere.

## Table 3:  Some Reservoirs of Carbon

| Reservoir | Quantity Stored (billion tonnes) |
|---|---|
| Atmosphere | 750 |
| Soils and organic matter | 1,600 |
| Terrestrial vegetation | 540-610 |
| Coal | 3000 |
| Oil & gas deposit | 300 |
| Dissolved organic matter | 700 |
| Surface water | 1020 |
| Deep water | 40,000 |
| Marine sediments & sedimentary rocks | 66,000,000 – 100,000,000 |

The first thing to notice from Fig. 19 and the tables is that man's emissions through fossil burning are puny — only 3% to 4% of natural emissions. Figure 20 presents the results graphically, showing annual $CO_2$ flows compared to our production of $CO_2$ from burning fossil fuels (set equal to 1 in the graph). Note from Tables 2 and 3 that terrestrial plant growth is enough to consume all of the atmosphere's $CO_2$ in about 12 years.

It is of interest that the actual *measured* increase in atmospheric $CO_2$ is 3.3 billion tonnes per year [20], only 60% as much as we put into the atmosphere. (On a personal note, I recall reading a coal journal in my dad's office in the late 1940s or early 1950s saying that scientists had no idea where all that $CO_2$ from coal burning was going, as it certainly was having negligible effect on the atmosphere.)

## Annual Carbon Flow (fossil burning = 1)

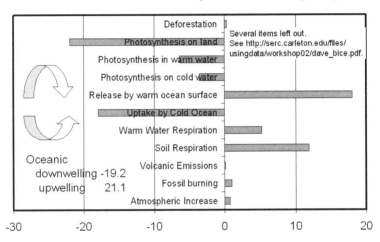

Figure 20: Annual carbon flow, using fossil burning = 1, emissions
to atmosphere to the right, and removal from atmosphere to left.
Many items from Fig. 19 are left out.

Let us now return to a point made by Al Gore, namely that the $CO_2$ concentration has never (before very recently) been higher than 300 parts per million, whereas since 1958 it has risen from 315 ppm to about 380 ppm. We need to ask why the ice core measurements were made in Antarctica, why the current data are measured at Mauna Loa, and whether the two sets of readings can realistically be compared.

The first question is easy. They measured $CO_2$ ice-core concentrations in Vostok, Antarctica, because that's where the ice is. (There are similar measurements from Greenland ice cores.)

Mauna Loa was chosen as a good spot to measure $CO_2$ concentration because it's at high elevation (over 11,000 feet, 3350 meters) so that local vegetation does not interfere with readings, way out in Hawaii, far away from man's influence, and in a rather breezy area.

Both places are free of influence from everything.

Except one.

The oceans.

Hawaii is in the tropics. The ocean is actually cooler (near 70 °F, 21 °C) than one would expect from its latitude, but warm nonetheless. Antarctica is surrounded by oceans that are just a little above freezing. As we have seen, the warm oceans emit $CO_2$ and the cold oceans absorb $CO_2$. It stands to reason, therefore, that the two data sets are actually measuring $CO_2$ from entirely different environments, and that they cannot be directly compared. One simply *expects* that the readings from Antarctica will be lower than those from Hawaii; how could it be otherwise? Now, why should we be surprised that current readings at tropical Mauna Loa are higher than historical readings at polar Antarctica?

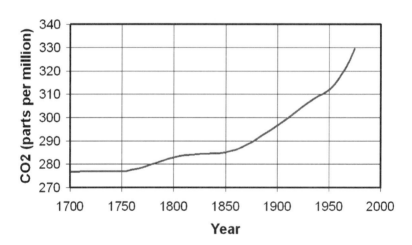

## CO2 at Law Dome

Figure 21: **Carbon dioxide concentration (parts per million) measured in Antarctic ice at Law Dome [21]. The dates are somewhat uncertain, because $CO_2$ isn't captured until ice actually forms from packed snow, and the delay time isn't well known. But the three-century rise is unmistakable.**

Primer on $CO_2$ and Climate

Figure 21 shows $CO_2$ concentration in Antarctic ice cores since about 1700 (measured at Law Dome by Etheridge *et al* [21]). When snow falls, it doesn't trap $CO_2$; in fact, the $CO_2$ isn't captured until the snow has built up enough to start packing the subsurface parts into ice, and the delay time can only be estimated. Nevertheless, it is certain that $CO_2$ concentration has been rising since before the Declaration of Independence, and long before humans' burning of fossil fuels could have had any measurable effect.

It is "obvious" to some that the increase in atmospheric $CO_2$ seen in Fig. 2 is due to human consumption of energy from fossil fuels. After all, we burn coal, oil, and natural gas, and the combustion produces $CO_2$. Moreover, the annual increase in atmospheric $CO_2$ corresponds approximately to the amount produced by fossil-burning.

But in the past, $CO_2$ levels have increased and decreased with no help whatsoever from humans. Looking at Fig. 21, one wonders just what the $CO_2$ concentration would be if there had been no combustion of fossil fuels. There has been a continuous increase in $CO_2$ since about 1775, decades before Richard Trevethick's first practical steam locomotive in 1804 and America's 1829 "Stourbridge Lion" (imported from England) made its debut.

*Somehow,* $CO_2$ concentration has increased *and* decreased with no help from mankind, and has done so for at least a half-billion years. Obviously there is interplay between processes that produce $CO_2$ and those that remove $CO_2$ from the atmosphere.

# $CO_2$ and Temperature

Armed with the background on $CO_2$ and global temperature, what can we say about the relationship between the two?

For one, $CO_2$ is a greenhouse gas, a gas that absorbs outgoing infrared radiation and re-emits it in random directions, some back toward the earth. It is the gas the Kyoto Protocol attempts to control in order to keep the earth from overheating. It is the gas that Al Gore, James Hansen, Stephen Schneider, and others rail against, a product of fossil-fuel burning that is supposedly causing unprecedented heating of Planet Earth. (To date, they have not yet begun a campaign against the most significant greenhouse gas, which is water vapor.) Figure 22 [3] has frequently been used to show how strongly the two are correlated.

But the greenhouse effect is only one relationship between temperature and $CO_2$ concentration. The other one is that warm water emits $CO_2$, as noted above. The greenhouse effect is one of theory (in the sense of *how much?*); the emission by warm water is one of experimental fact.

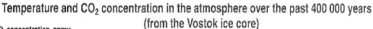

## Temperature and CO₂ concentration in the atmosphere over the past 400 000 years (from the Vostok ice core)

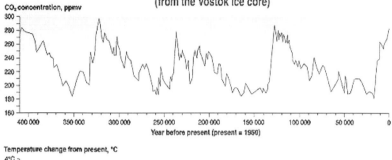

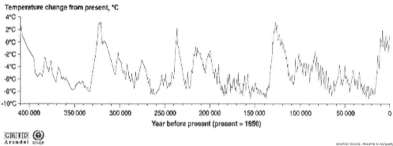

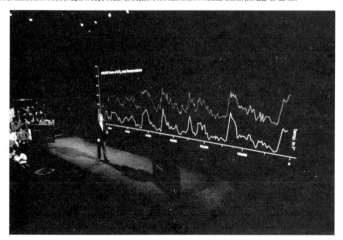

**Figure 22:** (Upper) Ice-core data from Vostok, showing $CO_2$ concentration and temperature for the last 400,000 years. (Lower) Al Gore waxing eloquent about the similarity of the shapes of the curves.

Primer on $CO_2$ and Climate

There is no doubt whatsoever that temperature and $CO_2$ concentration in Fig. 22 are correlated. But there is an even *better* correlation between temperature at a given time and $CO_2$ concentration *later* (by several hundred years). One can see from the NOAA website [4] that the data are available only for about 1000-year intervals, so it is not possible to be precise in this matter.

Remember that we asked, in reference to Fig. 5, where the $CO_2$ came from when concentration rose and where it went when concentration dropped. Now we know. It came from the oceans that were warming, and went to oceans when they were cooling.

Oh, and what's the cause of the warming and cooling? Think of that 800-pound gorilla in the kitchen, the sun that is the source of all our warmth, all light, and all photosynthesis. The sun is pretty steady, but not *absolutely* steady. For example, there were very few sunspots recorded during the Little Ice Age.

Moreover, there are periodic changes in the orbital parameters, such as the shape of the orbit, the tilt of the earth's axis, and whether the southern or northern hemisphere is in summer when the earth is closest to the sun. (This consideration is very important, since most of the land mass is in the northern hemisphere. At present, the earth is closest to the sun in early January.) These so-called *Milankovitch cycles* [see ref. 22 for example] are the primary forces driving the heating and cooling of the earth shown in Figs. 18 and 22.

## Seeing the Atmospheric Effect

Figure 22 may indeed show the atmospheric effect, but not in the simple-minded "greenhouse-gas" similarity between the shapes of the temperature curve and the $CO_2$ curve. Much has been made of the notion that the earth is 33 °C warmer than a hypothetical isothermal spherical stone in Earth's orbit would be if it reflected 30% of incoming sunlight.

The 33-degree difference is usually attributed entirely to the greenhouse effect, but the comparison is false, as eloquently noted by Gerlich and Tscheuschner [23]. In the first place, you cannot ignore the atmosphere, even in the total absence of greenhouse gases, simply because the atmosphere has its own heat capacity and dynamics. More importantly, you cannot ignore the oceans, even if $H_2O$ were not a greenhouse gas. Water *droplets* in clouds retain earthly heat, and somewhere near 20% of the sun's heat that arrives at the surface evaporates water. Furthermore, the clouds reflect incoming sunlight, as do ice and snow, thereby influencing the overall reflectivity (*albedo*) of the earth. A change in albedo from 30% to

29% would raise the temperature of the earth by 1 °C, all other things being equal.

For purposes of discussion, we will refer to the sum of all local effects as *atmospheric*, recognizing that *some* of that effect is actually due to greenhouse gases.

For the following discussion, we will ignore short-term solar variations, and consider only the long-term Milankovitch cycles, which we will call the *astronomical effect*. At times, the orbital changes are such as to bring the earth out of its ice ages; at others, they cause the earth to cool down.

The atmospheric effect is unidirectional, always causing the earth to be warmer than it would be without the atmospheric effects present. When we compare two different times when the temperature is the same, the greenhouse warming effect is the same, and presumably the other atmospheric effects are the same.

When astronomical effects cause the earth to warm up, the atmospheric effect works in the same direction, adding its warming effect. When astronomical effects cause the earth to cool, the atmospheric effect works in the opposite direction to the cooling, thereby slowing the rate of cooling.

Figures 18 and 22 show several major temperature fluctuations during the last 400,000 years. In all cases, the temperature rises toward a peak faster than it falls from the peak. As the temperature rises, it is an atmospheric-*enhanced*, astronomically driven rise. As the temperature falls, it is an atmospheric-*delayed*, astronomically driven decrease. In other words, when the temperature is rising, it is rising fast because the astronomical effect and the atmospheric effect pull in the same direction. When the temperature falls, the astronomical effect and the atmospheric effect work in opposite directions, so that the fall is not as fast as the rise. Again, the atmospheric effect here is that due to *all* atmospheric phenomena combined, such as thermal insulation, the water cycle, and GHGs.

Very roughly, the astronomical effect is about 2.5 times as great as the atmospheric effect, as one can determine by expanding the graphs and measuring slopes. This ratio applies, of course, only at the peaks of the curves, namely at the onset of and departure from, interglacials.

During the descent to ice ages, the earth has cooled down by 10 °C to 11 °C. A small stone of 30% albedo in Earth's orbit would be about 33 °C colder than the present earth, so it is fair to say that the atmospheric effect moderates the temperature even when $CO_2$ concentration has been cut to about 160 ppm (Fig. 5), and $H_2O$ concentration has been drastically reduced.

## Logarithmic Response

Not all $CO_2$ increments have the same effect on global temperature. In simplest terms, if there were no $CO_2$ in the air, then if some given amount of $CO_2$ were added to the air, it would block (say) 90% of the IR in the part of the spectrum where $CO_2$ absorbs it. If that amount of $CO_2$ were subsequently added to the atmosphere, it would be mathematically impossible to remove another 90% of that IR. In other words, each incremental amount of $CO_2$ added to the atmosphere produces ever less warming effect. Figure 23 shows the characteristics of exponential growth (like a bank account growing with compound interest) and logarithmic growth. No numbers are given; the important difference is just the shapes of the curves.

For the mathematically inclined reader, this decrease in response with each increment of $CO_2$ concentration is a logarithmic phenomenon. If the $CO_2$ concentration increases exponentially in time, then the overall effect is a linear increase in atmospheric temperature. (See A Few Technical Comments, page 54 *et seq.*)

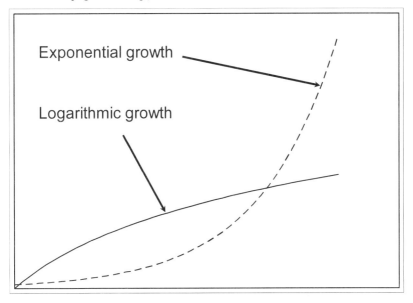

**Figure 23: A schematic drawing to show the distinction between exponential growth and logarithmic growth. As you move toward the right, the quantity grows and moves up the vertical axis.**

## Retroactive Causality

There are several principles of causality:

1. The cause must come before the effect. (Wet sidewalks don't cause rain.)
2. Not everything that comes before an effect is a cause. (Summer does not cause winter.)
3. Often, there is no such thing as *THE* cause. (Most two car collisions are caused by mistakes on the part of both drivers, and often upon weather conditions, highway conditions, and perhaps a third car that caused both of the others to swerve.)
4. Correlation is not causation. (Since the 1940s, the dramatic drop in the incidence of polio has been accompanied by an equally dramatic increase in the number of galaxies we have discovered.)

Figure 22 shows what looks like a pretty good correlation between $CO_2$ concentration and temperature. Given the model that increasing $CO_2$ causes the earth to heat up, one would suppose that "when there is more carbon dioxide, the temperature gets warmer," as Al Gore said. (Grammatical point: things get warmer or cooler, but temperatures increase or decrease.)

We know that $CO_2$ is a greenhouse gas, but we also know that warm oceans are a source of $CO_2$ and cold oceans are a sink. It is worthwhile to contemplate whether the earth warmed up and cooled down because of Milankovitch cycles or other reasons not related to $CO_2$, but that the warming and cooling oceans added or removed $CO_2$ from the atmosphere.

Fortunately, the record exists in the Antarctic glaciers, and has been elucidated. Researchers in at least two studies [24, 25] have studied the timing in detail at Vostok, using also data from Law Dome, and have found that the temperature changes occurred *before* the $CO_2$ changes.

> "High-resolution records from Antarctic ice cores show that carbon dioxide concentrations increased by 80 to 100 parts per million by volume $600 \pm 400$ years *after the warming* of the last three deglaciations." [emphasis added.]
>
> Fischer *et al* [24]

To put it fairly, but bluntly, to believe that $CO_2$ was responsible for the deglaciations of the past 400,000 years is to believe in retroactive causality, that the future can affect the past. Upon hearing this, Al Gore might commit posthumous suicide.

# Global Warming Models

Scientists working in laboratories set up experiments wherein everything is identical from one case to the next except for one single parameter that can be controlled. For example, car-safety experts may run identical cars with identical crash dummies into identical barriers, varying only the speed of the car between runs, in order to investigate the effect of speed. Alternatively, they may hold the speed constant and adjust the timing of the air bag.

No such luxury is available to global-warming modelers. Nobody can hold everything constant, while varying only the $CO_2$ concentration, for example.

In other words, *it is impossible to perform the well established procedures of laboratory science on the climate system. Nobody has done it. Nobody can do it. Nobody will do it.*

*All climate models are based on unperformed experiments for which the modelers presume to know the answer.*

Modelers try to account for all of the changing variables, with some adjustable parameters ("fudge factors") thrown in to account for the change. For example, if the temperature of the sun rises by 20 degrees, then the temperature of the earth ought to rise by one degree, *all other things being equal*.

Most adjustable parameters are not known well at all, so the modelers revert to curve-fitting. For example, one variable is snow cover, averaged over the earth, which affects the albedo (reflectivity) of the earth. The change of temperature caused by a change in albedo will be represented by a parameter $A$. Another causative agent is dirt on the surface of the snow, which *decreases* albedo; assign it a parameter $B$. One identifies many, perhaps hundreds, of changes that can conceivably cause changes in the earth's temperature, and assigns parameters $C, D, E...$ to them. Then, by using the weather records (thousands or millions of numbers), one can set up equations to solve for $A, B, C, D, ....$ When the job is done, the modeler can say with some pride that the model works at predicting past temperatures.

There are several problems here. In the first place, the models are all somewhat different, and they wind up with different values for the parameters. As a consequence, predictions of future temperatures vary *widely*. In the second place, there is no reason to believe that the same parameters will hold true ten years hence, because the parameters are not based on fundamental physics and chemistry. It is mere curve-fitting.

A friend attended a Ph.D. oral for a history student. There was some event that certainly happened, but nobody was certain whether it occurred on one particular date or another. The student decided to take the numerical average. Believe it or not, global warming alarmists do the same, in averaging the results of model outputs.

A third problem is that with enough adjustable parameters, it is possible to get a nice fit even if an important phenomenon is left out of the calculation entirely. For example, cosmic rays cause ionization, producing nucleation sites for $H_2O$ condensation, often causing high-altitude cirrus clouds. High solar activity causes the sun's magnetic field to increase near the earth (150 million kilometers — 93 million miles — away!), with the result that fewer cosmic rays arrive at the earth, and fewer cirrus clouds result. These events are left out of the models, but the fudge factors compensate anyway.

There are further problems with climate models (Global Circulation Models, or *GCM*s, as they are known to exegetes.) They make entirely the wrong predictions in at least three regions.

## *Arctic Regions*

We refer to both polar regions as "arctic regions," although they have entirely different environments. At the North Pole, the weather is largely controlled by the ocean currents, and the ice floats on water. Antarctica is a continent whose average elevation is the same as the average elevation of Colorado. Weather conditions for the vast majority of the continent ("East Antarctica," or "Greater Antarctica") are controlled by the air.

The largest, driest desert on Earth is Antarctica. The air is so cold that it can hold only extremely small amounts of water vapor. For example, at –60 °C and 100% relative humidity there is only 0.05% as much $H_2O$ in the air as there is at room temperature and 100% humidity. As a result, the major greenhouse gas — indeed the *only* GHG — in Antarctica is $CO_2$. Therefore, an increase in $CO_2$ concentration in Antarctica has a much greater effect than the same increase in the tropics, where $H_2O$ vapor is abundant. (Think of one voice in the shower versus one voice in a choir.)

But what do the data show? In Antarctica, the satellite temperature record [11] shows the land temperature changing at the rate of –0.09 °C/decade, in other words, *decreasing* when all models should show it increasing. At the North Pole, the air temperature is warmer to begin with (because of the lower altitude), so the effect of increasing $CO_2$ should be less than in Antarctica. However, the Northern Arctic air temperature is *increasing* at 0.44 °C/decade [11]. The climate models are at a loss to explain the polar data.

## *Violent Storms*

The source of energy for hurricanes is warm water, but warm water in and of itself does not cause hurricanes. One thing to understand is that if the entire earth were at one single temperature, there would be no storms whatsoever, whether that temperature be high or low. In fact, it is temperature *gradients* that cause storms. For example, a violent cyclonic storm has persisted on Jupiter, whose cloud-top temperature is an ultra-frigid –148 °C (–234 °F), for at least 300 years. Even at that temperature, it is temperature *differences* that drive storms.

According to climate models, the greatest warming should be at the poles. That warming should *decrease* the temperature gradient and *decrease* the frequency and violence of storms.

## *Aerosols*

Aerosols are fine solid or liquid particles suspended in a gas (air, for our purposes). According to global warming models, they have a mitigating effect. With more $CO_2$ emissions come more aerosols (such as tiny soot particles), though we are steadily reducing aerosol emissions. The atmospheric aerosols reflect sunlight, thereby reducing the amount of sunlight reaching the surface, hence acting to cool the earth. Indeed, this was the source of the worries in the 1970s when Stephen Schneider and others tried to convince the world that human activities were driving the world toward the next ice age. [See Fig. 24 from ref. 26]. Collins *et al* say, "Overall these aerosol effects promote cooling that could offset the warming effect of long-lived greenhouse gases to some extent." [6]

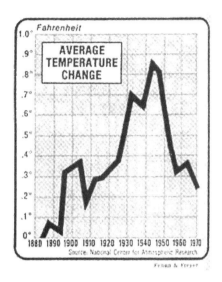

**Figure 24:** **Graph showing imminent global cooling, taken from** *Newsweek* **[26].**

It is generally believed that atmospheric $CO_2$ becomes rather uniformly mixed throughout the atmosphere, so that there is no distinction between Northern Hemisphere and Southern Hemisphere $CO_2$ concentrations. Aerosols, however, don't remain in the atmosphere very long, so they tend to be concentrated in the Northern Hemisphere, where most are produced.

Consequently, according to the climate models, atmospheric warming should be greater in the Southern Hemisphere (fewer aerosols) than in the Northern Hemisphere. However, the satellite record [11] shows the opposite. From the beginning (December 1978) to June 2007, the rate of temperature rise has been 0.22 °C/decade for the Northern Hemisphere and 0.07 °C/decade for the Southern Hemisphere [11].

A simple fact has escaped the attention of the modelers, namely that not all aerosols are the same color as pyroclastic dust from volcanoes. Satellite measurements have confirmed that dark-colored aerosols from polluted areas *absorb* sunlight and cause heating. [27]

## Oceans and Atmosphere

Collins et al [6] say, "In the ocean, we clearly see warming trends, which decrease with depth, as expected. These changes indicate that the ocean has absorbed more than 80 percent of the heat added to the climate system: this heating is a major contributor to sea-level rise."

Primer on $CO_2$ and Climate

We'll discuss sea-level rise below, but note in the meantime that global warming models do not make any such prediction. All of the models predict that the atmosphere — indeed, the *upper* atmosphere — should warm *first*, and it isn't happening.

Figure 25 shows the disagreement between models and observations for tropical regions, where models all say that the temperature should be rising as the altitude increases to about 10 km, whereas the data show a distinct *decrease* in that region [29].

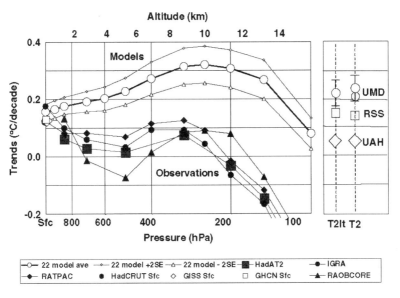

**Figure 25: Temperature trends in °C per decade, versus altitude, measured in pressure units on bottom scale, and in kilometers on top scale. "Sfc" means surface. The models say that the temperature trend should be positive, and more so up to 10 km altitude; data show decreasing trends.**

## *The Water Cycle*

The most important GHG is water vapor, and clouds have a profound effect on climate, as reflectors of sunlight, as greenhouse blankets, and as the carrier of 20% of the sun's energy that reaches the earth. You would think that climate modelers would have to understand the water cycle before making grandiose proclamations about understanding climate.

But you would be wrong. We have heard for many decades about how $CO_2$ is causing the dreaded global warming, and the climate community knows precious little about the water cycle. In fact, a satellite was launched in 2006 for the sole purpose of studying the nature of the water cycle. [30]

"The practice of staring at clouds will take on new dimensions with the impending launching of two satellites designed to make the *first global survey of cloud properties* that affect weather and climate, scientists said Wednesday," reports *The New York Times* [30]. The program is called *CloudSat.*

To emphasize the point, let us quote directly from the *New York Times* article.

"Graeme Stephens of Colorado State University, the principal investigator, told a news conference on Wednesday at the Jet Propulsion Laboratory in Pasadena, Calif., that although just 1 percent of Earth's water existed in the atmosphere, *little was known about its overall role in climate.*" [emphasis added]

Warren E. Leary, *New York Times* [30]

Let me quote directly from the article Stephens wrote for *The Denver Post* [28].

"CloudSat has provided the *first real information* on the fraction of clouds that produce precipitation. Over the Earth's oceans, CloudSat has shown that *precipitation is much more common than was previously thought*, due to the fact that precipitation over oceans is extremely hard to measure and the light rain that often falls has been completely missed by satellite observations until now. *Weather and climate models fail to predict this precipitation...*

"Weather and climate-prediction models predict that the *majority of rain* that falls *comes from deep thunderstorms*. CloudSat *has revealed that this is not the case*, and instead the observations show that a large proportion of rain falls from much shallower clouds.

"CloudSat has provided new insights on the greenhouse effects of clouds, identifying where and when clouds trap heat in the atmosphere and where and when they increase the amount of heat lost from the atmosphere to space. This dynamic trade-off between heating and cooling is *one of the basic controls on global climate and the new knowledge gives scientists better tools* to estimate future climate.

"[T]he *complex interplay* between the polar surface and polar clouds *can now be studied for the first time.*

"Clouds also exert a large influence on the climate of our planet, not only by way of the precipitation they produce but also by *altering the Earth's greenhouse effect in ways that are not yet fully understood.*" [Emphasis added]

Now, at long last, we will have apparatus in place to *begin* a decades-long process of learning about atmospheric $H_2O$. To quote a memorable line from the owl in an old Pogo comic strip:

"**All** in good time ... We ain't the sloppy kind what tries to do **two** things at once. Up to **now**, we jes been **talkin'**... but when we starts **thinkin'** 'bout this ... **stand back!**"

Walt Kelly (1954)

## Correlations

All scientists are familiar with the phrase *Correlation is not Causation.* Just because two changes occur nearly simultaneously does not imply that one caused the other. You can easily show a correlation between the nominal price of bread and the number of observed moons of planets in the solar system during the last 50 years.

But there is no other basis for asserting that the observed temperature rise is caused by man's consumption of fossil fuels. That it *might* be so, because $CO_2$ is a known absorber of IR, is a model-dependent conclusion with no certain mathematical validity. (There is no doubt that $CO_2$ is a greenhouse gas, but there is great doubt about the expected *amount* of warming.) That it *might* be so because temperature has risen while $CO_2$ concentration has risen, is a conclusion based on correlation and a large number of adjustable parameters. There is no honest basis whatsoever for the conclusions [6] of the IPCC (2001) that it is "more than 66 percent probable" or of the IPCC (2007) that it is "more than 90 percent probable" that "most of the warming since the mid-20th century was attributable to humans."

## HIGWIGC

Perhaps the most ludicrous prediction is that of Human-Induced-Global-Warming-Induced-Global-Cooling (HIGWIGC). If the earth heats up, humans are responsible. If the earth cools down, humans are responsible.

The best one can say of this model is that it is like playing 5-card stud with 52 cards wild.

# Solar Activity

The effect of the sun on the earth is not limited to the usual "blackbody" spectrum, consisting mainly of visible light, infrared, and ultraviolet, from which the "should-be" temperature of the earth is calculated. There are solar coronae whose temperatures are in the millions of degrees, greater or lesser numbers of solar storms made visible by sunspots, and magnetic field storms that disrupt radio communications on earth and actually extend out to and beyond Mars' orbit. Variations in solar activity cause 20% variations in the flux of cosmic rays coming from all directions in space [31]. It has long been known that the Little Ice Age was simultaneous with the *Maunder Minimum*, an extended period characterized by the near absence of sunspots.

The influence of the sun on the earth is obvious; however, the influence of the variations of solar activity is *not* obvious. Sunspots block a certain amount of *visible* light, yet there is an enhancement of ultraviolet. Rays coming from the far reaches of the universe cause ionization in the upper atmosphere, and water vapor condenses on the ion tracks. When the solar magnetic field is strong, some of those cosmic rays are deflected away from the earth, and there is a decrease in high-altitude cirrus cloud cover. Those clouds have some effect on the albedo of the earth, but also have a greenhouse effect.

Though scientists have long known that the sun's behavior is not constant, the first indication of a method to determine past behavior was disagreement between ages calculated from carbon-dating and those known from other techniques. For example, tree-ring data are unambiguous, one year per ring. Carbon-14 "ages" at various depths into tree cores have been at variance with the count of the rings.

Carbon-14 is created from nitrogen-14 by high-energy protons in the upper atmosphere [32]. It decays radioactively with a 5,730-year half-life. When a tree grows, it absorbs carbon dioxide from the atmosphere, and some of that carbon is C-14. Once that (part of) the tree stops growing, the fraction of C-14 begins to decline. Since the production of C-14 varies slightly with solar activity, the starting concentration of C-14 varies, and that is why the carbon-14 ages do not always agree with tree-ring ages. Or, reversing the thinking, one can use the disagreement between known ages and C-14 ages to determine past solar activity.

There is another cosmogenic isotope, beryllium-10, that can also be used. It is extremely rare and has a half-life of 2.6 million years. Therefore, on the scale of a few tens of thousands of years, radioactive decay causes no measurable effect on the quantity of Be-10 present in ice cores. Any variations in concentration are due to production rate alone, hence to cosmic ray flux alone.

Measurements of Be-10 have shown that solar activity since about 1940 is the highest it has been in the last 1150 years [33]. Moreover, the sun's coronal magnetic field has doubled in the last 100 years [33].

There is yet another phenomenon that is probably related to solar activity. By studying ice cores, sea-surface temperatures, deposits of pollen and seeds in lake beds, and many other phenomena, scientists have discovered the existence of a 1500 ± 500 year cycle that goes on and on, through ice ages and interglacials [16]. There is no *known* 1500-year solar cycle. Still, it is hard to imagine anything other than the sun that could explain the 1500-year cycle seen in temperatures and plant growth that persists through a half-million years of glacial-interglacial cycles.

## *The Time Series*

As the sun slowly changes, the earth's climate shortly follows. That fact is neither new nor in dispute. However, it is not so obvious from known data that more rapid changes on the sun cause changes in the earth's climate. The reason is that the oceans, the glaciers, the land mass, and the atmosphere might all respond, but not at the same rate. Therefore, any short-term correlations are hard to detect.

Nicola Scafetta and Bruce West undertook a new analysis briefly described in *Physics Today* [34]. The method was to look at the time series for solar flares and compare it to the time series for the earth's temperature anomalies.

An analogy of this method is as follows. Imagine that you look at a novel and count the number of times that one *e* is followed in the next (non-blank) space by another *e* (as in *feel*), the number of times that the letter count from one *e* to the next is two (as in *there*), and so forth. You could plot the distribution on a graph and possibly fit a formula to the result. (It would certainly not be a bell curve.) You could do the same for the letter *j*, and the distribution would be different. (How often do you find *jj*?) In other words, the spacing distributions would be different for the two letters.

Now look at the distribution in times between solar flares. As it happens, they fit a distribution that fits a fairly simple formula which says that the probability $P(t)$ of a time interval of $t$ follows a simple inverse relationship of the form $A/t^\alpha$, where $A$ is an uninteresting proportionality constant that increases with the number of years of data. The number $\alpha$ is characteristic of the distribution of time intervals, and happens to be 2.14.

The investigators also looked at the time series for earthly atmospheric temperature anomalies, and found that they fit a distribution given by the same formula, with closely matched characteristic values. The values of $\alpha$ were 2.11 globally, 2.20 for the Northern Hemisphere, 2.09 for the Southern Hemisphere, 2.11 over land, and 2.06 over the ocean. It would be amazing if all of those distributions were so nearly equal by coincidence. The inescapable conclusion is that the short-term fluctuations in solar activity drive short-term fluctuations in atmospheric temperature.

Assembling the long term fluctuations and the short-term fluctuations, Scafetta and West show that the sun is the major driver of Earth's climate. They say, "The non-equilibrium thermodynamic models we used suggest that the Sun is influencing climate significantly more than the IPCC report claims. … We estimate that the Sun could account for as much as 69% of the increase in Earth's average temperature, depending on the TSI [Total Solar Irradiance] reconstruction used."

And what of the grandiose claims that the IPCC makes for their conclusions? In 2001, the IPCC claimed that it is "more than 66 percent probable" and in 2007, claimed that it is "more than 90 percent probable" (meaning "extremely likely") that "most of the warming since the mid-20th century was attributable to humans." [6]

But if the same temperature data can be explained by fluctuations in solar activity, there is no certainty whatsoever — *zero* —that the IPCC's computer models provide the only explanation.

It's garbage in, gospel out.

# Glaciers

Glaciers advance. Glaciers retreat. It all depends on the time scale.

The last ice age "ended" about 18,000 years ago. The mile-high glaciers in North America retreated. There are no glaciers left standing on Manhattan Island.

During the Little Ice Age, glaciers advanced. The Thames River froze during winter. People ice-skated on frozen rivers in The Netherlands.

Glaciers bear a certain resemblance to the Great Sand Dunes in the San Luis Valley of Colorado. Snow, like sand, is subject to the whims of weather. Piles of snow or sand are *always* being eroded away by wind and water. If that were the only force of nature at work, neither sand nor snow would remain in place for long.

The details of the dynamics of the Great Sand Dunes involve local phenomena; suffice it to say that there is interplay between the forces that add to the dunes and those that diminish them. For glaciers, the interplay is more complicated, because the wind can blow snow to or away from the glacier, but has much less effect on snow that has been compressed into ice. Ice and snow can melt and/or sublimate. But the basic idea is just the same. Some phenomena add to glacial mass; others reduce glacial mass.

Nobody is surprised that water flows from rivers into the ocean, and there are no "documentaries" showing the gushing water and bemoaning the loss of water from the land. Glaciers are flowing *ice*, and the ice flows toward the sea. When enough ice accumulates, it falls of its own weight, and rather spectacularly: Al Gore's *An Inconvenient Truth* shows the "calving," implying that it is an unusual phenomenon due to global warming.

Antarctica has been warming around the edges, although the interior has gotten colder. Perhaps, the warming of the adjacent seas can be partially blamed on a newly discovered active volcano whose presence was revealed after the overlying ice broke off and drifted away [35]. The volcano is located at the northernmost tip of Antarctica.

Mount Kilimanjaro's glaciers have been diminishing, but Mount Kilimanjaro is not getting warmer; it is getting colder. The diminution of its glaciers has to do with the lack of snow, which in turn is due to the lack of moisture in the air. Forest removal is the underlying cause. That may well be a human-caused environmental problem, but it has nothing to do with atmospheric $CO_2$.

Figure 26 from Orlemans [36] (with James Watt's birth added) shows representative glacier sizes from around the world since the 1700s. Note that glaciers have been retreating since before thirteen colonies became the United States.

And what about Greenland? A Danish study [37] of 247 of the 350 glaciers on Disko Island off the coast of Greenland report that 70 percent of the glaciers have been shrinking regularly since the end of the 1880s at a rate of around eight meters per year.

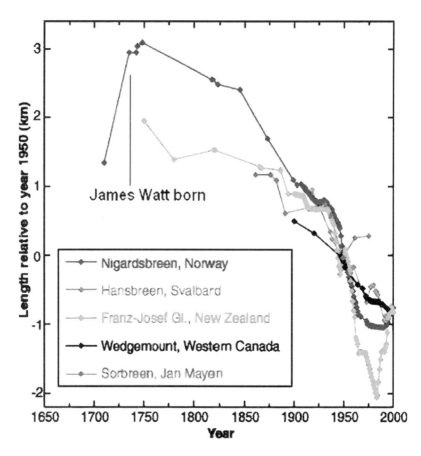

Figure 26: A representative sample of glacier sizes relative to their sizes in 1950. See Orlemans [36]. For the most part, glaciers are retreating as they have been since about 1750. James Watt's birth can rightfully be considered the dawn of the Industrial Age, but really large releases of $CO_2$ date only from about 1945.

Mars also has polar ice caps of $CO_2$ (a,k,a, dry ice), *and they are diminishing*. The time span is much shorter — encompassing only one Martian year — but Fig. 27 [from ref. 38] shows loss of polar ice from 1999 to 2001. The pictures do not have enough resolution to see the Martian SUVs that are the source of the problem.

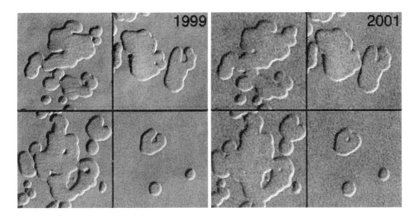

**Figure 27: Polar ice caps on Mars. Left 1999; Right 2001 (Same time of Martian year). Notice the widening of valleys, disappearance of peaks.**

# Sea Level

Yes, sea level is rising. Again, we will look at sea level on several time scales. Most recently, sea level has been measured by satellite using buoys out in the ocean. Figure 28 [from ref. 39] shows results of those measurements from 1993 to the present. From 1994 to 2006, sea level rose at the rate of about 2.8 centimeters (1.1 inch) per decade. It is a tribute to modern satellite technology that such measurements are indeed possible, because the amount of rise is minuscule compared to daily variations.

Collins *et al* [6] say, "Since 1993 satellite observations have permitted more precise calculations of global sea-level rise, now estimated to be 3.1 ± 0.7 mm per year over the period 1993 to 2003." Big deal. Chalk it up to the short time scale.

Figure 29 shows a mean-sea-level marker carved by Captain Ross in a bay in Tasmania in 1841 [40]. The length of the marker is a half-meter, and tidal range from the mean level is less than a meter. The photograph, taken in 2004, shows the marker at low tide.

On a longer time scale (Fig. 30, from ref. 41), sea level has risen 18 centimeters (7 inches) in 100 years. Measurements of sea level are always dicey, but there are adequate historical records from all seafaring nations to produce the time series seen in Fig. 30. Figure 30 shows, around the early 1980s, an increase of 12 mm per year, and a decrease of the same magnitude, and again shows how ludicrous it is to get excited about changes over short time periods.

During the time periods in Figs. 28 and 30, the change of sea level has been minor. However, since the glaciers of the last ice age began to recede (Fig. 31), sea level has risen quite dramatically, 120 meters (400 feet) in the last 18,000 years. Figure 31 [42] shows that the rapid rise ended about 7,000 years ago and since that time the rise has been slow but steady. The current situation is just a continuation of that 7000-year slow rise.

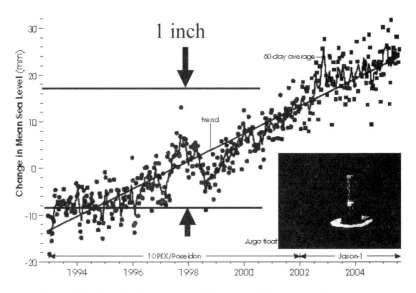

**Figure 28: Sea level as measured by two different satellite systems, TOPEX/Poseiden from 1993 to early 2001, and Jason-1 since then. The vertical axis is the change in sea level measured in millimeters. One inch of rise is shown for comparison.**

Figure 29: Mean sea level in a bay in Tasmania in 1841, as carved by Captain Ross. The marker length is a half-meter, and tidal range is less than a meter.

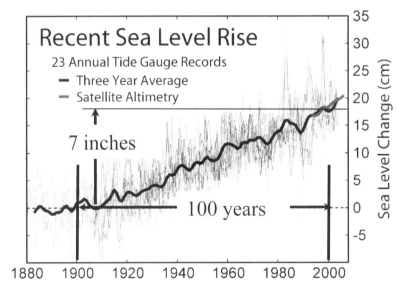

Figure 30: Sea level from the early 1880s to the present.

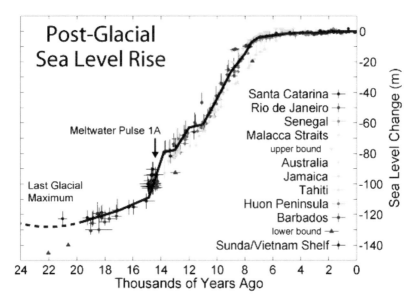

Figure 31: Sea level since the last glacial maximum. Note the rise of about 120 meters (400 feet).

# The "Consensus"

A nice thing about science is that people eventually have to come to agreement about facts. Scientists also have to come to agreement about calculations. There is no room for personal prejudice about the product of 8 multiplied by 7.

On the other hand, scientific advances almost always come when somebody goes against conventional thinking. When the new paradigm becomes understood, it becomes conventional thinking.

But agreement among scientists does not guarantee that what they agree upon is correct. For one example (actually cited by Al Gore), continental drift was once pooh-poohed by geologists, and is now universally accepted. My point is simply that consensus is irrelevant. Drifting continents do not care one whit what the scientists think. The universal acceptance of continental drift now is no more proof of continental drift than the earlier denial of continental drift was proof of a static earth. There are other examples of "consensus science" that are worthy of mention.

- In 1626, "Consensus Science" killed "witches" for a crop-destroying frost. ("The resumption of witch-hunting in the 1560s was accompanied by a debate about weather-making, because this was the most important charge against suspected witches." [43]

- 1800s: "Consensus Science" killed women in childbirth because physicians refused to take the advice of Viennese physician Ignas Semmelweis, who had shown that simple hand-washing had reduced infections when doctors attended childbirth. "Semmelweiss' colleagues demonstrated the traditional reluctance of the medical profession to accept new ideas, particularly when the new ideas meant admitting doctors had caused countless unnecessary deaths. Semmelweiss was fired from the clinic. Not until 30 years later were his ideas about the prevention of childbed fever put into widespread practice." [44]

There are more recent examples:

- *Conservation of energy "proved" that the earth can't be older than 300,000 years.* The "proof," due to Lord Kelvin, rested on incomplete physics, and is known as the "Kelvin fallacy."
- *The laws of electromagnetic radiation "proved" that atoms can't exist.* In 1913, physicist Niels Bohr used different assumptions and succeeded in predicting the hydrogen spectrum.
- *Berringer Crater was not caused by a meteor impact.* "This phenomenon always used to get people worked up and excited. Up until the mid-1800's scientists scoffed at the idea that rocks could fall from the sky. It wasn't until the mid-1900's that the Berringer Crater in Arizona was proved to be a meteor impact crater!" [45]
- Stomach ulcers are caused by "stress." No. Bacteria.
- *Life cannot exist deep in the ocean.* No. Tube worms live at thermal vents.

Al Gore is a firm believer in consensus. In Fig. 32, he is saying that of 928 scientific articles about global warming in a recent study, no scientists "disagreed with the scientific consensus that we're causing global warming and that it's a serious problem." The actual paper, written by Naomi Oreskes [46], was seriously flawed, but not *that* flawed. What Oreskes said was, "Without *substantial* disagreement, scientists find human activities are heating the earth's surface" [emphasis added].

British social anthropologist Benny Peiser was suspicious of even that conclusion, and did his own Internet search [47]. Using broader criteria, he found nearly 12,000 papers; using her more restricted criteria, he found 1,117 papers. But he actually read them, and the results were not at all what Oreskes had said. Of the 1,117 papers, a whopping 13 explicitly endorsed the "consensus view." Some 322 *implicitly accepted* the view, and simply worked to figure out the consequences to flora and fauna. Forty-two percent made no link whatsoever — direct or indirect — to human activities. Finally, 34 of the papers either cast doubt on — or outright rejected — the view that human activities are responsible for climate changes in the last 50 years.

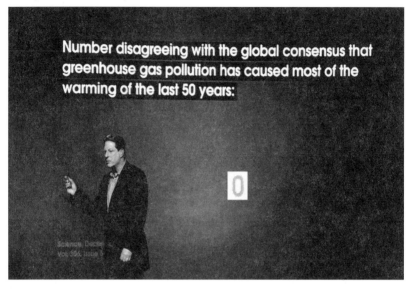

**Figure 32: Al Gore refers to a discredited paper about scientific consensus.**

In other words, the claim that overwhelming scientific consensus exists is not only irrelevant, but just plain wrong.

# Mosquitoes And Other Vectors

Al Gore tells us that Nairobi, Kenya was founded because it was just above the "mosquito line" (See Fig. 33). In fact, "Nairobi owes its foundation to the construction of the Railway" [48]. But just in case Gore thinks that high altitude is a barrier to mosquitoes, I'd be glad to have him walk shirtless along a stream I used to hike in the Rockies above 9000 feet elevation. Maybe we could hike over Mosquito Pass at 13,185 feet in elevation. Nor are mosquitoes limited to temperate zones. The mosquitoes in the far north are *ferocious*, as they would have to be if they are to make a living sucking blood from thick-skinned grizzly bears.

Paul Reiter is professor at the Institut Pasteur in Paris, chief of its Insects and Infectious Disease Unit, and a specialist in the natural history and biology of mosquitoes, the epidemiology of the diseases they transmit, and strategies for their control. In his talk at the 2008 International Conference on Climate Change, he said that malaria-carrying mosquitoes were already so prevalent in Nairobi when the railway station was installed that the railway was urged to put the station elsewhere.

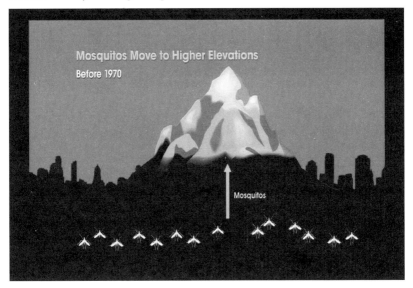

**Figure 33: Al Gore's drawing of his alleged "mosquito line."**

The mosquito-borne disease malaria has been on the rise for decades, but it has absolutely nothing to do with global warming. The use of DDT had reduced malaria cases in many countries to a mere handful annually, but the *ban* on DDT has caused millions of malarial deaths, and the number is increasing. No surprise here.

Curiously, the location of the world-famous Mayo Clinic in Minnesota is due to the presence of malaria [50] in *Indiana*.

> "The elder Mayo was an English immigrant who attended Indiana Medical College in LaPorte and then practiced medicine in Lafayette, Indiana. Apparently, his attraction to Minnesota was due, in part, to the absence of malaria in the territory, an affliction that was called the 'scourge' of Indiana's Wabash River valley. Mayo had witnessed the recurring debilitating chills and fever that plagued residents of the valley each summer and characterized 'hell' as 'a place where people have malaria.'"

*Mayo Clinic Proceedings* [50]

# The Gore Syndrome

Al Gore and the IPCC shared the Nobel *Peace* Prize in 2007. It is not a prize for physics, nor for chemistry, nor for geology, nor for any science whatsoever. The Prize puts Al Gore right up there with Yasser Arafat.

A recent review by Rush Holt of *An Inconvenient Truth* in *Science* [51] has applauded Al Gore's success in getting the public to believe that "climate change is under way and that it is induced by humans. ... Gore can be given as much credit as anyone for these developments."

The review would be more appropriate for a journal of advertising than of science, for it discusses — *praises* might be a better term — the methods and successes in persuading the public. It says, "Most significant, Gore structured the presentation with a shrewd recognition of how people learn and how they make decisions. He tells stories, personal stories."

The stories that Rush Holt praises are tear-jerkers designed to make the audience sympathetic to Al Gore. At one point Gore whines that Congress wouldn't listen to him. (Sheesh! I thought *I* was arrogant! Just exactly what makes him so well qualified that Congress should listen to him? He had one course in college physics?) He has a tear-jerker about his son being hit by a car. He bemoans losing the election in which he won the popular vote. He laments "all the bad things they've said about Al Gore." He presents a heart-wrenching story about how the family used to grow tobacco. Absolutely none of this garbage is about global warming. It's about Al Gore.

The reviewer, Rush Holt, a U.S. Representative from New Jersey's 12th district,[2] goes on to say, "I believe Gore's science solid." This remarkably naive line is to be expected from the run-of-the-mill scientific ignoramuses in Congress. But it is utterly shameful when coming from one of Congress's only two physicists.

The alarming fact is simply that *Science* would publish such a review. Alarming, but not surprising. *Science* has long since given up its objectivity.

## *The Propaganda Effort*

Skeptics of Anthropogenic Global Warming (AGW) theory are frequently accused of being shills of the oil or coal industries. Indeed, an ABC News report [53], relying on the Greenpeace's Research Director Kurt Davies, attempted to show that Professor Fred Singer is "linked" to "a

---

[2] In the First Edition, I said mistakenly that Rush Holt is not a scientist. Actually, he holds a Ph.D. in physics from NYU.

whole web of organizations, many funded by oil and coal companies that have spend millions trying to convince the public there's a real scientific debate about global warming." Singer immediately responded with a cogent letter beginning,

> "I share the anger expressed in nearly 100 postings (so far) at the shoddy handling of my interview aired on March 23: It was an appalling display of bias, unfairness, journalistic misbehavior, and a breakdown of ethical standards. It used prejudicial language, distorted facts, libelous insinuations, and anonymous smears. I urge you to read the postings; only one person offered any support to ABC, as far as I can see."

Singer did once receive an unsolicited $10,000 dollar donation from Exxon. That's hardly enough to support a theory of conspiracy with a whole web of scurrilous industries.

**Figure 34: Very costly electronic billboards at Times Square advertising global-warming gloom-and-doom.**

On March 4, 2008, I managed to get a few photographs of a huge electronic billboard at Times Square (the very building where they drop the ball on New Year's Eve), advertising climate-gloom-and-doom. It pictures Beijing, China, in 2075 under desert sand dunes. Other informative pictures showed the Amazon rainforest in 2064 looking like New York City, and London under ocean waves in 2092. The end of the ad said, one word at a time in a glaring set of blinding flashes:

# FIND OUT WHAT YOU CAN DO

Obviously, the cost for running such advertising must be horrendous, so I inquired. For one of the signs (I don't know which) it costs $40,000 per month to run two minutes worth of advertising every hour. The price decreases for larger quantity, and amounts to something like $700,000 per month for full-time advertising. The gloom-and-doom ad ran about a quarter to a third of full time.

If you are interested in finding out who provides the money for such expensive propaganda, go to www.hsbc.com/CommitToChange. Evidently, HSBC (an international bank) is in bed with numerous "environmental" groups. That's where you *start* following the money.

Who stands to gain from the propaganda campaign? People who think that polar bears are cuddly creatures certainly have an emotional investment, misplaced as it is, in creatures that have survived through some very warm interglacials. But the real beneficiaries are alive and well, producers of nothing, but buyers and sellers of nothing but artificial, fear-generated "credits" for not producing $CO_2$.

In a recent interview with Leslie Stahl on *CBS's 60 Minutes*, Al Gore returned to his mantra that people who dispute that mankind is causing the earth to warm up precipitously are equivalent to flat-earthers. To convince the public that we have an urgent problem, he has begun a $300 million propaganda campaign [54].[3]

> Three-hundred million dollars is a truly massive amount of money to throw at a propaganda effort, and one is entitled to ask, *"Who benefits?"*

## A Few Technical Comments

The solar intensity at Earth's orbit is about 1,370 watts (thermal) per square meter. If a black sphere were in the orbit, it would absorb all of that radiation over the area $\pi R^2$ facing the sun. If the sphere were small enough to be all at the same temperature, it would radiate heat away in all directions from the entire surface area of the sphere, $4\pi R^2$, following the Stefan-Boltzmann law, according to which every square meter would radiate 5.67 $\times$ 10$^{-8}$ watts, multiplied by the fourth power of the sphere's absolute

---

[3] Of course, Al Gore calls it "advertising," as if he were selling a product. (Ask your doctor if Carbon Credits are right for you!)

temperature. At equilibrium, the sphere's temperature would be 279 Kelvin, or 6 °C.

The earth's *albedo* (overall reflectivity) is about 30%. If our small sphere had that albedo, it would absorb 70% of the solar flux, and its temperature would be 255 Kelvin, or − 18 °C. An assumption here (and it seems to be valid) is that almost every solid (no matter the color) radiates with near 100% efficiency in the far infrared, which is the radiation emitted from bodies of the temperatures indicated.

The earth's average temperature is about 15 °C; many people have remarked (incorrectly) that the earth is therefore 33 °C warmer than it would be without the greenhouse gases. But the comparison of a small isothermal sphere with *no* atmosphere and no oceans, with an earth that *has both*, and is certainly not all at one temperature is a bit of a stretch [23]. About 20% of the sun's heat causes water to evaporate into the sky. At high altitude, the vapor condenses, depositing its heat into the surrounding air, and descends to the ground as rain, hail, sleet, or snow. That is, a major heat transport mechanism involves water, quite independently of any infrared absorption.

Figure 35 shows the radiant intensity of ideal blackbodies at two different temperatures, 325 K (52 °C, 126 °F) and 260 K (−13 °C, 9 °F), representing Phoenix, Arizona on a hot summer day, and the highest temperature ever recorded at the South Pole, respectively. Absent any atmosphere, and absent any oceans, the curves represent outgoing infrared (IR), sometimes called Outgoing Longwave Radiation (OLR). This is the radiation that interacts with $H_2O$ and $CO_2$, both of which can absorb and re-radiate the radiation.

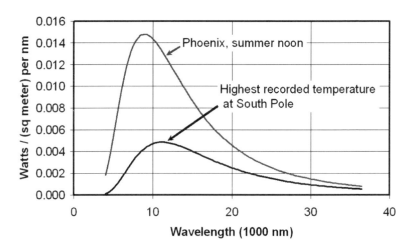

**Figure 35: Blackbody radiation curves for (nearly) extreme temperatures found on Earth.**

How strongly do those greenhouse gases absorb the OLR? We need to look at the absorption *cross-sections*. These numbers tell how big the atoms look to OLR on its journey to outer space. Fig. 36 shows results of measurements [55]. Water vapor absorbs IR over a wide range of wavelengths, and $CO_2$ absorbs very strongly, but in a narrow band. The larger the cross-section, and the greater the density of the absorbing molecules, the shorter the distance the IR can travel without being absorbed.[4]

---

[4] The intensity will drop to about one-third (exactly, $1/e$) at a distance $L$, given by $L = 1/(n\sigma)$, where $n$ is the number density of absorbing molecules, and $\sigma$ is the cross section. For example, if the density is $3 \times 10^{19}$ per cubic centimeter, and the cross section is $10^{-21}$ cm$^2$, then $L$ is only 30 meters.

Primer on $CO_2$ and Climate

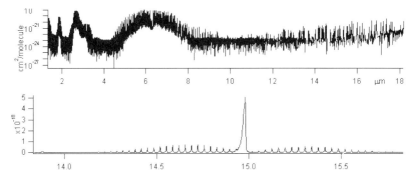

Figure 36: Infrared absorption cross sections for $H_2O$ (upper) and $CO_2$ (lower), in $cm^2$ per molecule. The upper graph is logarithmic; the lower one is linear. Both horizontal scales are in micrometers. Only wavelengths of greater than about 5 micrometers are of interest because below that (see Fig. 36), the emissions from earth are negligible.

Now we combine the two sets of information. Figure 37 shows the results, wherein we shade the wavelength ranges where the cross section is large enough to absorb within a few kilometers of the surface. We assume that the atmosphere is 1% water vapor, which will be too high for arctic regions and too low for damp tropics.

From Fig. 37, it is obvious why $CO_2$ cannot be a particularly effective greenhouse gas. It absorbs only a very small fraction of the OLR, and is transparent to the rest.

> By way of comparison, on Venus, where the $CO_2$ concentration is nearly 250,000 times as high, and where the surface temperature is extreme — about 480 °C, 900 °F — $CO_2$ is a very effective greenhouse gas. The high surface temperature emits strongly at shorter wavelengths than the 5 micrometers considered here, and $CO_2$ can absorb radiation over a very wide range of wavelengths. The absorption per molecule isn't so strong, but the number of molecules is so high that almost all surface radiation is absorbed.

In Global Warming jargon, the additional absorption of IR and random re-emission by an increase in absorbing gas concentration produces a *forcing* equivalent to so many additional watts per square meter of surface caused by the additional concentration. The forcing, in turn, depends upon the concentration through the formula $Forcing = \Delta F = A \ln\left(\dfrac{C}{C_0}\right)$, where $C_0$

is some initial concentration, $C$ is the concentration at another time, and $A$ is a constant that depends upon the absorptive properties of the gas. For $CO_2$, the constant $A$ is generally acknowledged [10] to be 5.35 W/m$^2$. If the concentration doubles ($C = 2* C_0$), then the forcing becomes 3.7 W/m$^2$.

## Blackbodies at 325 K and 260 K

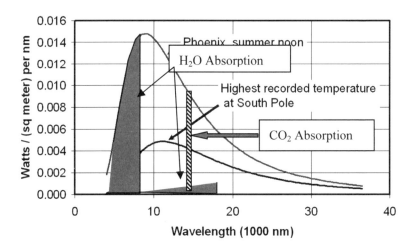

**Figure 37: The absorption characteristics of Fig. 36 superimposed on the blackbody curves of Fig. 35 in the wavelength range of greater than 5 micrometers (5000 nm). The shaded areas represent absorption of that wavelength within about 3 km of the surface.**

Given an amount of forcing, what temperature rise should result? One introduces a variable $\lambda$ which translates that forcing into a temperature change. Therefore the temperature rise $\Delta T$ is given by

$$\Delta T = \lambda \Delta F = \lambda A \ln\left(\frac{C}{C_0}\right)$$
$$= \text{Const} * \ln\left(\frac{C}{C_0}\right) \tag{1}$$

showing that the temperature rises *logarithmically* with concentration. And if the $CO_2$ concentration rises exponentially with time, then the temperature should rise linearly with time.

Here is where the mud hits the fan. Any reasonable calculation of $\lambda$ from known data results in a value of $\lambda$ between 0.1 and 0.2 [56]. (The units are °C per $W/m^2$.) The corresponding temperature rise for a doubling of $CO_2$ concentration is an un-frightful 0.4 °C to 0.8 °C. Not surprisingly, global-warming alarmists use higher values for $\lambda$, typically in the range of 0.5 to 1, with no apparent justification for doing so, other that "expert opinion."

That's just the beginning. If the earth warms up a wee bit, and if there are some powerful positive-feedback mechanisms — things that conspire to heat the earth further and further, rather like the phenomenon of a microphone placed in front of a speaker — then there would be a "tipping point" beyond which the earth would heat up uncontrollably. Positive feedback mechanisms would include the disappearance of snow, exposing underlying soil that absorbs more of the sun's heat; and the increase of $H_2O$ vapor, owing to increased evaporation and the ability of warm air to hold more water vapor. Possibly there are other positive feedback mechanisms.

Negative feedback mechanisms work the other way. Increased cloud cover increases the albedo and reflects more incoming sunlight. Rain, snow, sleet, and hail are mechanisms that cause that most important GHG to leave the atmosphere.

Overall, is the feedback positive or negative? Clearly, if the earth's climate system had such a "tipping point" where positive feedback would lead to disaster, then that tipping point would have been reached a long time ago. Surely during the last few hundred million years, *something* would have heated the earth enough to reach that tipping point. If nothing else, the very high $CO_2$ levels during the Jurassic would have propelled the climate toward boiling oceans. It didn't happen. It won't happen.

# Concluding Remarks

The difference between weather and climate is only the time scale. Weather varies from day to day, week to week, month to month, and season to season. We expect summer to be warmer than winter, but this summer is never identical to last summer. This decade is always different from the last decade, and so on. We are not presently experiencing the climate that characterized the Little Ice Age (roughly from 1300 to 1850), or that of the last great ice age that lasted the better part of 100,000 years. Generally, one would use the term *weather* to refer to the situation over short time scales, and *climate* to refer to average conditions over many years.

The climate, just like the weather, changes whether we like it or not. Nobody — absolutely nobody — disputes that climate has changed continually during the 4.6-billion year age of the earth. There is also no dispute that the earth has been warming (with ups and downs) since the Little Ice Age. That is called *global warming*, a term that also applies to at least 20 warming events that one can see in Fig. 18. Global warming is, by definition, climate change, but climate change is not necessarily global warming. The frequent descents into ice ages were obviously changes in climate, but were cooling, not warming.

The global-warming debate is thus not about whether the climate changes or whether the earth is presently warming (though if the satellite record had begun in 2001, some might argue that there is no warming at all). The debate is about *anthropogenic* global warming (AGW) and *anthropogenic* climate change. (The term *human-induced* could be used here, but never use four syllables when five will do.)

Every single day, records of some kind are broken somewhere. With a few hundred thousand reporting stations, each with data on temperature, rainfall, snowfall, hail, lightning, wind speed, drought length, cloudiness, length of rainfall period, insect infestations, crop growth, and dozens of other things that are weather-related, the probability approaches 100% that some record somewhere is broken today.

In an earlier era, the news reporter would just comment on the new record; nowadays, the news reporter blames the situation on global warming. Decades ago, say, the only people who knew about or cared much about the weather in Pocatello, Idaho, were the people who lived there. Now, if they experience a heat wave, *The New York Times* will report the event to the world. Not a day goes by without some news outlet obsessing about the devastating effects of global warming.

For example, Hurricane Katrina was but one of a series of devastating hurricanes that occurred in 2005, and there were endless pronouncements about how that was a glimpse of things to come it humans didn't stop driving SUVs and using air conditioners. When there were *no* land-falling hurricanes in 2006, the news media had to dream up other things to blame on global warming, hinting all the while that humans were to blame.

The causal link between human activities and global warming is feeble at best, amounting to nothing more than some weak correlations and some very incomplete computer models. Yes, $CO_2$ is a greenhouse gas, and yes, greenhouse gases keep the earth warmer than it would be without them. But when it comes down to knowing *how much* warming can be expected from *how much* $CO_2$, the models can only estimate what would happen *if nothing else changed*.

In particular, the models fail on several counts. They have no understanding of the water cycle. They predict the greatest warming at the South Pole, which has actually been cooling. They predict the greatest atmospheric warming in the upper troposphere, where it is not observed. They predict that the Northern Hemisphere, with all of its aerosols (assumed by the models to be reflective), should warm more slowly than the Southern Hemisphere, in contradiction to the facts. They provide no explanation of the source of the $CO_2$ that allegedly had something to do with bringing the world out of the ice ages; especially, they offer no explanation as to why the changes in $CO_2$ concentration came *after* changes in temperature. The models exhibit no agreement among themselves about which areas on earth would become drier or wetter.

Remember this: the hysteria about global warming is all traceable to the *models* (and their well-funded zealots), not to actual data.

Human emissions of $CO_2$ amount to roughly 3.5 percent of all $CO_2$ emissions. In other words, Mother Nature emits about 30 times as much $CO_2$ as we do. But the most important greenhouse gas is $H_2O$, which is about 100 times as abundant in the atmosphere worldwide as $CO_2$ is. The GCMs are at a loss to how to handle $H_2O$. *If* humans are responsible for global warming, there is no proof, either in the data or in the models.

We have addressed the question of whether global warming is real (yes, the earth has been warming up) and whether humans are responsible (to some minor extent, probably; to a large extent, no). The remaining two questions are whether global warming is good or bad, and whether (if global warming is bad) there is anything we can do about it.

A warmer earth results in a longer growing season in the temperate zones. Higher $CO_2$ concentration amounts to more plant food in the air. Both imply more food available for the humans on earth. Of course, the disaster-a-day news media have ignored those benefits, but concentrated on the fact that poison ivy grows better in a high-$CO_2$ environment [57].

By contrast, the Little Ice Age destroyed grain harvests in Northern Europe and wiped out grape vines in England. (History can't tell us who invented bread, but the loss of wine grapes did not go unrecorded.) Throughout Europe, Great Britain, and the Russian steppe, there was massive starvation and hunger-induced disease. Millions of people died prematurely, but not from poison ivy exposure. (What a relief!)

It is clear, then, that global warming is not all bad, and it is extremely clear that ice ages are devastating. Certainly, some places would be adversely affected by warming and others would benefit. (So what's new?) In the Holocene Climate Optimum, most of the Sahara was green — not a jungle, but far from being the desert that it is today. But there may well have been areas of the earth that had worse conditions than they have today.

It is interesting that the global-warming alarmists inveigh against $CO_2$, but never face the obvious fact that the fuels that produce $CO_2$ are the very ones that allow civilization to survive. As noted by Douglas Lightfoot [52], we need energy far more than we need to control $CO_2$ emissions. Every time we move something, heat something, cool something, grow something, shape something, melt something, or basically do anything at all, we use energy. The alarmists want — desperately — to gain control over all energy-using activity, which means all of life.

## Proposed Solutions

But assume, just for fun, that (A) human emissions of $CO_2$ are causing global warming; and (B) that global warming is bad (perhaps catastrophic). Is there any remedy? We begin with propagandistic and legalistic approaches.

### Heavy Hands

*Kyoto Lite*

The Kyoto Protocol called for the US to reduce its $CO_2$ emissions to 7% below 1990 levels by the year 2008; the rest of the world had its own targets. With few or possibly no exceptions, the nations of the world did not meet their targets. Whereas the US did not ratify the Protocol (in spite of Al Gore's pressure to do so), some other countries did. Still, $CO_2$ emissions worldwide increased, aided in part by Kyoto signatories.

Kyoto's effect on $CO_2$ emissions would have been about as effective as a screen door on a submarine. The world's fastest growth centers — India and China — were exempt, as were the Third World countries, who are struggling to get into the twentieth century before the rest of us get out of the twenty-first. Overall, the $CO_2$-emission reductions would have been utterly negligible compared to overall emissions, especially compared to those of Mother Nature. Of course, everybody knew that, even Kyoto proponents. If reductions in $CO_2$ emissions were negligible, perforce the effect on worldwide temperature (in *any* model) would be immeasurably small.

*Kyoto Calorie-Laden*

What Kyoto proponents had in mind was a little seduction, followed by something a little more severe: a reduction of $CO_2$ emissions by 80 percent, for which they are now lobbying. We quote from *Speigel Online* [58]:

> "A bitter fight lies ahead: If a massive change in energy consumption and heavy production is to take place, traffic and consumption would be have [*sic*] to be undergo painful reductions. By the middle of this century,

$CO_2$ emissions need to be reduced by up to 60 and 80 percent in industrialized countries, said [UN Climate Change head] Yvo de Boer.

"Sixty to 80 percent? The climate change regulations of the 1990s don't even come close to bringing about that kind of reduction."

*Most* of our energy — about 86 percent in the US — comes from combustion of coal, petroleum, and natural gas. Of the three, on a per-energy basis, coal produces 1.81 times as much $CO_2$ as natural gas, and petroleum produces 1.25 times as much as natural gas. In terms of $CO_2$ production, the US produced 2,614 billion tonnes of $CO_2$ from petroleum, 1,178 billion tonnes of $CO_2$ from natural gas, and 2,138 billion tonnes of $CO_2$ from coal in 2005 [59]. It is often argued that we should switch coal uses over to natural gas. Doing so could hypothetically reduce our $CO_2$ production by 16 percent. But even a complete switch of *both* coal and petroleum to natural gas would only reduce our $CO_2$ production by 25%, and that is assuming that there is no increased demand for energy.

## Economic Schemes

Various schemes have been advanced for reducing our "carbon footprint," the most pernicious of which is the cap-and-trade emissions idea. In countless news releases, it is promoted as being a free-market approach, but no description could be farther from the truth. It begins with *cap*, which amounts to an imposed maximum amount of emissions that you (the generic *you*, an individual, a company, an international corporation, a city, a country…) could emit. Some governmental or international agency, presumably, would make that decision for you.

The *and-trade* part of the scheme amounts to the right to buy "carbon credits" from a generic somebody who didn't use up his agency-established allocation. It is somewhat like getting a balanced diet by eating doughnuts while paying somebody to eat spinach for you. Al Gore has already proudly bought some carbon credits to atone for his jet-setting. None of it has reduced carbon emissions.

But there is something more sinister on the horizon. It may seem from the hype that the entity with carbon credits for sale might be a corporation that has "gone green," making all sorts of efficiency improvements. But on the international scale, the cheapest carbon credits will always come from third-world dictatorships that can rake in money by keeping their economies suppressed. Think of paying Idi Amin of Uganda or Robert Taylor of Liberia for the right to be productive.

# The Supreme Court and the EPA

The Environmental Protection Agency has not declared $CO_2$ a pollutant. Massachusetts, egged on by environmental extremists and joined by several other states, has sued the EPA in federal court to force the EPA to declare $CO_2$ a pollutant and then to regulate it. (Translation: to restrict fossil fuel consumption.) The federal court agreed with the EPA, but the case was then pushed to the Supreme Court.

The case before the Supreme Court was historic, in that Massachusetts' standing as a "sovereign state" allowed it to make claims that it was being unduly harmed by "global warming" and all of its attendant horrors.

> In addition, Justice Stevens said, Massachusetts was due special deference in its claim to standing because of its status as a sovereign state. This new twist on the court's standing doctrine may have been an essential tactic in winning the vote of Justice Kennedy, a leader in the court's federalism revolution of recent years. Justice Stevens, a dissenter from the court's states' rights rulings and a master of court strategy, in effect managed to use federalism as a sword rather than a shield [60].

The Supreme Court did not rule that $CO_2$ is a pollutant, but that the EPA has to present a scientific finding one way or the other. If it is not a pollutant, subject to EPA regulation, then the EPA must provide a scientific justification. If the EPA finds scientific evidence that $CO_2$ is a pollutant, then it must regulate it. The EPA may not remain mute on the subject.

But it is clear that the Supreme Court *did* have a bias against the EPA for not regulating $CO_2$ (in "tailpipe emissions" and so forth).

> Massachusetts, one of the 12 state plaintiffs, met the test, Justice Stevens said, because it had made a case **that global warming was raising the sea level along its coast**, presenting the state with a **"risk of catastrophic harm"** that "would be reduced to some extent" if the government undertook the regulation the state sought [60]. [Emphasis added]

The case made by Massachusetts was obviously pure, 99.44% fact-free. Exactly what sea-level rise were they talking about?

Thomas Phipps, Ph.D. of Urbana, Illinois, has written the following letter to *The Gazette* describing the situation.

> A group of state attorneys general, including the one from Illinois, is currently suing the Cotton Mathers of the Environmental Protection Agency (EPA) for inadequate fanaticism in enforcing last year's politically correct ruling by the Supreme Court that 'carbon dioxide and other greenhouse gases are air pollutants.'

Carbon dioxide is a permanent gas, known to produce no cancer in any form of animal life, known to be essential to all forms of plant life, without which all life would perish from the earth within months, and blessedly present as a saving 0.038 percent of the atmosphere. To classify it as an air pollutant merely because it is a greenhouse gas calls for similar action in classifying water vapor, a vastly more effective (indeed, the principal) greenhouse gas.

One pictures the Supremes, Canute-like, commanding the seas to cease evaporating ... and the attorneys general fuming because the EPA drags its feet in enforcing the edict.

It seems about time to abandon George Washington's noble experiment in democracy and turn over our government to the children – who are well-indoctrinated in the global warming panic. The result will be another Children's Crusade. That will surely be even more entertaining than the same spectacle, led by the graybeards of our Supreme Court, and flogged by 17 state attorneys general acting with the support of our taxes.

## Engineering Dreams by Non-Engineers

Scientists and engineers think in terms of technical solutions. After all, whether there are international laws and sanctions or not, it is state-of-the-art engineering that ultimately determines whether proposed solutions are practical. Non-technical folks generally pay no heed to such constraints as laws of physics. ("I'll manage the idea part; your job is to go make it possible.")

### Dream 1: Becoming More Efficient

There is nothing either unique or new about becoming more efficient. It is (and has long been) often the strongest argument of a salesman that a company can save lots of money by using more efficient machines or better insulation. Accordingly, efficiency improvements abound (and have for centuries), and we ought to be proud of them instead of cowering in front of efficiency nannies.

But there is a delusion at work here. Conservation is not a source of energy, anymore than dieting is a source of nutrition. The energy we use every time we move something, shape something, or change something in any way must come from *somewhere.*

Apart from that, there is no evidence that any efficiency improvement has ever led to a permanent overall reduction in energy use. (How much energy do we use every year in the hundreds of millions of efficient computers, compared to what we would use if we had only slow, inefficient, power-hungry vacuum-tube-type computers?)

## Dream 2: Sequestration

It all sounds so simple. Just equip coal-fired power plants with equipment to sequester $CO_2$ so that it doesn't get into the atmosphere. The $CO_2$ from coal combustion weighs roughly 3.5 times as much as the coal itself. If that $CO_2$ is chemically bonded (say to calcium, from some non-existent calcium mines), the weight increases further. A molecule of $CaCO_3$ weighs almost twice as much as one of $CO_2$. So, for every rail car carrying 100 tons of coal that goes into a coal-fired plant, there would have to be 700 tons of $CaCO_3$ removed from the plant. (We are assuming, of course, that there is some easy way to collect that $CO_2$ and react it with calcium in the first place.)

We all learned as children about the three states of matter: gas, liquid, and solid. Carbon dioxide doesn't fit that paradigm. At atmospheric pressure, $CO_2$ exists either as gas or solid, the latter (known as dry ice) at a very cold temperature of about $-78.5$ °C ($-109$ °F).

At higher pressures, however, $CO_2$ can become a liquid or a solid. At the freezing point of water, $CO_2$ liquefies at a little over 30 atmospheres of pressure, a pressure that exists about 300 meters (1000 feet) below the surface of the ocean. At 10 °C, the required pressure is about 45 atmospheres, the pressure 450 meters (1500 feet) deep in the ocean. But putting $CO_2$ at that depth into the ocean certainly does not guarantee that it will stay there. The ocean has streams of current in addition to storms (ask any submariner). Only in deep trenches might there be some hope of sequestering $CO_2$ as a liquid. And there is no place in the ocean deep enough to retain $CO_2$ as a solid, because $CO_2$ doesn't solidify until the pressure is at least 3300 atmospheres.

Let's continue the dream anyway. Suppose we decide to pump $CO_2$ from coal-fired power plants into the Aleutian Trench, the Middle American Trench (off the Pacific coast of Costa Rica), or the mid-Atlantic Trench. And suppose we could capture it and pump it at the rate of about 1000 tonnes per hour — at every one of our 800 coal-fired power plants in the US. Exactly how do we get that $CO_2$ from New Mexico or Pennsylvania or Kentucky to one of those trenches?

## Dream 3: Renewables

The three main dreams in the media these days are photovoltaics, ethanol (from corn or perhaps switchgrass or other biomass), and wind. Of the three, only one produces energy that can reasonably be stored, and that's the biomass option. (Much more energy is available if the biomass is burned directly than if it is converted to ethanol.)

No matter how much research is done in what laboratories, nobody will be able to make the sun shine at night. Suppose, just for fun, that photovoltaic cells were highly efficient, very cheap, and already tied into the electrical grid. Suppose further that there were no cloudy days and no reason ever to do maintenance (even cleaning) of the PV cells. What would provide power at night, especially long winter ones?

There is only one way to store energy on a large scale, and that's through pumped hydro. There must be a system to pump water from a low-elevation reservoir up to a high-elevation reservoir when excess power is available. When additional energy is needed, the water stored in the high-elevation reservoir is then allowed to pass through turbines to generate electricity. The overall efficiency depends upon the lengths of pipe involved, and can be as low as 50% or presumably as high as about 80%.

There are some such systems in the US, and their net loss of electrical energy is only about 6-to-9 billion kWh per year. But the requirements are hard to meet. Where does one find adequate water, places for two reservoirs that are very different in elevation, and transmission lines to deliver the power to (say) New York City?

Industrial wind "farms" are highly touted as being clean, renewable energy, but they produce the lowest quality power on the planet. You wouldn't want to be on a wind-powered elevator when the wind speed dies while you're between floors. The wind industry is presently thriving, but only because of massive tax benefits, subsidies, and the willingness of some people to pay extra for small amounts of electricity generated by wind.

Wind and PV can *supplement* serious sources of energy, but can never stand alone as *the* energy sources. Consequently, they can't really make much of a dent in $CO_2$ emissions.

## Dream 4: Nuclear Fission (Uranium and Thorium)

Nuclear power has the capability of reducing $CO_2$ emissions while *also* providing power around the clock. And, yes, there is plenty of uranium to last for at least millions of years *if we use all of the uranium, not just the U-235* isotope. But there are two problems.

The first problem is that the anti-energy crowd has made the nuclear option sound like a frightening prospect. The costly — but in no way dangerous — Three Mile Island accident was used by the press to create hysteria. It put a halt to nuclear construction in the US. Far worse was the Chernobyl accident, which killed about 30 people and has had the press and anti-nukes fussing about thousands of hypothetical latent deaths. (All of us are in the state of latent death, come to think of it; it's a condition known as being alive.) Never mind that the Chernobyl reactor was of a design rejected in the US over 50 years ago, and never mind that there was no containment building. That accident has been seized upon as being proof that nuclear power is to be avoided at all costs.

The second problem is that without a long period of completely changing our energy infrastructure, nuclear power is good only for producing heat and electricity, not for running the transportation system. There is no hope of ramping up nuclear production enough to make dramatic cuts in $CO_2$ emissions in the foreseeable future.

## Dream 5: Nuclear Fusion

It is said of nuclear fusion that it is the energy source of the future and always will be. Fusion, of course, is the process by which the sun generates energy deep within its core. Also, we have demonstrated the process here on earth with the explosion of hydrogen bombs. The problem is to scale it down to some reasonable size.

There has been much research for the last several decades at many laboratories throughout the world. The purpose of the research is to acquire data that can be used to design fusion reactors. At the present, it looks as if the data are in hand for what could be the first energy-producing fusion reactor to be built in 20 years or so. Even if the project proceeds apace, it would amount to one reactor large enough to displace one or two large coal-fired power plants, but far from being able to reduce $CO_2$ production by any measurable amount. And if it is so successful that everybody (even the anti-energy crowd) agrees that it should be the one-and-only energy choice, it could not possibly be expanded fast enough to supply even half of our energy for at least 50 years.

## Dream 6: Hydrogen

We are told, correctly, that hydrogen is the most abundant element in the universe. The sun's energy comes from fusing hydrogen into helium. Hydrogen burns in air to form $H_2O$, simple, benign water vapor.

There are some major problems with hydrogen. The first is that there are no hydrogen wells. No place on earth can we drill a well and get hydrogen gas. Hydrogen is always bound up chemically, such as in $H_2O$, from which we must extract it — using more energy than we will be able to get back.

The second problem is that hydrogen is a gas. As a consequence, it has low energy density, in the volume sense. A liter of gasoline has roughly 37 million joules of energy available; a liter of hydrogen at atmospheric pressure has about 6,000 joules, roughly one six-thousandth as much as gasoline. To get decent energy density, it is necessary to subject hydrogen to extremely high pressure in very strong and heavy containers, or to liquefy it at –253 °C, only 20 °C above absolute zero.

A third problem with hydrogen is that it embrittles steel. It cannot be transported in ordinary steel tanks and pipes.

# A Final Note

A new manuscript by Gerhard Gerlich and Ralf D. Tscheuschner, entitled "Falsification of the Atmospheric Greenhouse within the Framework of Physics" [23] makes a very strong case against climate models, pointing out that the "atmospheric greenhouse effect" does not appear in any fundamental work of thermodynamics, in any work of fundamental work of physical kinetics, or in any fundamental work or radiation theory.

Gerlich and Tscheuschner find many errors of fundamental physics in climate models, including heat transfer from cooler bodies to warmer ones (by confusing reflection with re-radiation), totally ignoring thermal conductivity, totally ignoring friction is moving atmospheres, an incorrect assumption that a radiation field is a vector field, and assumed "radiation balance" where none occurs. The famous 33 °C temperature difference due to the supposed greenhouse effect arises from an illegitimate comparison of our earth with one that has no atmosphere. As well, necessary higher derivative operators (like the Laplacian) can never be represented on the grids with wide meshes that are used in climate models.

Oh, and how *does* a glass greenhouse work? Simply by restricting air flow. The late Petr Beckmann wrote in *Access to Energy* twice (Sept. 1977 and Feb 1979), and Gerlich & Tscheuschner have written in their recent paper that as early as 1909, R. W. Wood became suspicious of the standard explanation and did some measurements. He compared temperatures in identical insulated greenhouse boxes, one with regular glass and one with a rock salt window that is totally transparent to infrared. The sunlight going into the rock salt window was pre-filtered by a (distant) glass pane to block the *incident* IR. The temperatures achieved in the two boxes were identical within 1 °C, the limit of the measurement at the time.

"How big is the energy challenge of climate change? The technological advances needed to stabilize carbon-dioxide emissions may be greater than we think, argue Roger Pielke, Tom Wigley, and Christopher Green," says the editor's introduction to a very recent commentary in *Nature*, presumably speaking for himself. [61] The authors themselves are more correct when they say, "The technological challenge has been seriously underestimated *by the IPCC.*" [Emphasis added].

Every rational person has understood from the very beginning that strong reductions in $CO_2$ emissions would be nearly impossible to meet, and that people everywhere would suffer impoverishment with its attendant starvation and disease.

And for what?

# References

[1]  NOAA's    Earth    System    Research    Lab    at
     http://www.esrl.noaa.gov/gmd/ccgg/trends/co2_data_mlo.html
[2]  C.D. Keeling and T.P. Whorf, "Atmospheric carbon dioxide record
     from Mauna Loa, http://cdiac.ornl.gov/trends/co2/sio-mlo.htm
[3]  United    Nations    Environment    Programme    (UNEP)    at
     http://www.grida.no/climate/vital/02.htm, [data from ref 4].
[4]  NOAA    Satellite    and    Information    Service    at
     http://www.ncdc.noaa.gov/paleo/icecore/antarctica/vostok/vostok_co2.
     html.
[5]  Ernst-Georg Beck, "180 Years of Atmospheric $CO_2$ Gas Analysis by
     Chemical Methods," Energy and Environment, vol. 18, no. 2, 2007.
[6]  W. Collins, R. Colman, J. Haywood, M. R. Manning, and P. Mote,
     "The Physical Science behind Global Warming," Scientific American,
     August 2007.
[7]  Image:    Phanerozoic    Carbon    Dioxide.png    at
     http://www.globalwarmingart.com/wiki/Image:Phanerozoic_Carbon_
     Dioxide_png
[8]  R.A. Berner, "Paleo-CO2 and climate," Nature 7/9/92
[9]  "Carbon Dioxide," http://en.wikipedia.org/wiki/Carbon_dioxide
[10] Intergovernmental    Panel    on    Climate    Change    website    at
     http://www.ipcc.ch/
[11] University    of    Alabama-Huntsville    at
     http://www.nsstc.uah.edu/data/msu/t2lt/uahncdc.lt
[12] http://www.ncdc.noaa.gov/img/climate/research/2006/ann/glob_jan-
     dec-error-bar_pg.gif
[13] Mann, M.E., Bradley, R.S., Hughes, M.K., "Global-Scale Temperature
     Patterns and Climate Forcing Over the past Six Centuries," Nature
     392, pp. 779-787 (1988).; "Northern Hemisphere Temperatures
     During the Last Millennium," Geophysical Research Letters 26, pp.
     759-762.
[14] Stephen McIntyre and Ross McKitrick, "Corrections To The Mann Et.
     Al. (1998) Proxy Data Base And Northern Hemispheric Average
     Temperature Series," Energy & Environment, Vol. 14,· Number 6,
     2003, available on the web at http://winnetou.lcd.lu/physique/glo-
     bal/hockey_stick/mcintyre_02.pdf

[15] "Hockey Stick Hokum," editorial in The Wall Street Journal, 14 July 2006, available at http://online.wsj.com/article-/SB115283824428306460.html.

[16] S. Fred Singer and Dennis T. Avery, Unstoppable Global Warming: Every 1500 Years, (Roman and Littlefield, New York, 2007).

[17] Thomas J. Crowley, "Remembrance Of Things Past: Greenhouse Lessons From The Geologic Record" at http://www.gcrio.org/CONSEQUENCES/winter96/article1-fig2.html

[18] Dave Bice (Carleton University) at http://serc.carleton.edu/files/usingdata/workshop02/dave_bice.pdf

[19] See chart at United Nations Environmental Programme at http://maps.grida.no/go/graphic/the_carbon_cycle

[20] Global Commons Institute, "The 'Airborne Fraction' Of GHG Emissions Is Increasing In Addition To The GHG Emissions Themselves," http://www.gci.org.uk/briefings/rising_risk.pdf

[21] D.M. Etheridge, L.P. Steele, R.L. Langenfelds and R.J. Francey, J.-M. Barnola, and V.I. Morgan, "Historical CO2 records from the Law Dome DE08, DE08-2, and DSS ice cores" at http://cdiac.ornl.gov/trends/co2/lawdome.html

[22] Milankovitch cycles. See, for example, http://www.homepage.montana.edu/~geol445/hyperglac/time1/milankov.htm

[23] Gerhard Gerlich and Ralf D. Tscheuschner, "Falsification of the Atmospheric Greenhouse within the Framework of Physics," submitted to physics.ao.ph as arXiv:0707:1161ve (11 Sept, 2007).

[24] Hubertus Fischer, Martin Wahlen, Jesse Smith, Derek Mastroianni, Bruce Deck, "Ice Core Records of Atmospheric $CO_2$ Around the Last Three Glacial Terminations," Science, vol. 283. no. 5408, pp. 1712 – 1714 (12 March 1999)

[25] Nicolas Caillon, Jeffrey P. Severinghaus, Jean Jouzel, Jean-Marc Barnola, Jiancheng Kang, Volodya Y. Lipenkov, "Timing of Atmospheric CO2 and Antarctic Temperature Changes Across Termination III ," Science, vol. 299, no. 5613, pp. 1728 - 1731 (14 March 2003)

[26] Peter Gwynne, "The Cooling World," Newsweek April 28, 1975. Thanks to Prof. Emíle Knystautas of Univ. Laval for this article.

[27] "Aerosols Warm up the Atmosphere," *Chemical and Engineering News,* August 6, 2007, referring to *Nature* 2007, 448, 575.

[28] Graeme Stephens, "Reading the clouds: Colorado team's satellite makes strides," *Denver Post* August 26, 2007.

[29] David H. Douglass, John R. Christy, Benjamin D. Pearson, and S. Fred Singer, "A comparison of tropical temperature trends with model predictions," *Int. J. Climatol,* (2007).

[30] Warren E. Leary, "More Satellites to Explore Clouds' Most Intimate Secrets," *The New York Times* at http://www.nytimes.com-/2006/04/20/science/earth/20clouds.html?ex=1146196800&en=532b7 36906820673&ei=5070&emc=eta1, April 20, 2006

[31] Eigil Friis-Christensen, "Do Solar Variations Affect Our Climate?" http://esa-spaceweather.net/spweather/workshops-/SPW_W3/PROCEEDINGS_W3/friis-christensen.pdf

[32] "Radiocarbon dating" at http://en.wikipedia.org/wiki/Radio-carbon_dating and "Solar Variation" at http://en.wikipedia.org/wiki-/Solar_variation .

[33] Cambridge Conference Correspondence," with numerous references, at http://abob.libs.uga.edu/bobk/ccc/cc102203.html

[34] Nicola Scafetta and Bruce J. West, "Is climate sensitive to solar variability?" Physics Today, pp 50-51, March 2008. The work refers to two of their papers: Phys Rev. Letts. 90, D24S03 (2003) and J. Geophys. Res. 112, D24S05 (2007).

[35] Randolph E. Schmid, "Underwater Antarctic volcano found: Research ship documents apparently fresh lava flow," http://www.msnbc.msn.com/id/5023002/

[36] J. Oerlemans, "Extracting a Climate Signal from 169 Glacier Records," Science Vol 308, pp. 675-678 (29 April 2005).

[37] http://www.breitbart.com/news/2006/08/21/060821191826.-o0mynclv.html

[38] "Climate of Mars" at http://en.wikipedia.org/wiki/Climate_of_Mars

[39] http://earthobservatory.nasa.gov/Newsroom/NewIm-ages/images.php3?img_id=17300

[40] http://www.john-daly.com/

[41] "Sea Level Rise," at http://en.wikipedia.org/wiki/Sea_level_rise

[42] Post-Glacial Sea Level graph and description at http://www.answers.com/topic/post-glacial-sea-level-png

[43] Wolfgang Behringer,1999, "Climatic Change And Witch-Hunting: The Impact Of The Little Ice Age On Mentalities"

[44] "Chicago Maternity Center: 77 years of home deliveries...Will this be its last? (1972) http://www.cwluherstory.org/CWLUAr-chive/materncenter.html

[45] "The Astronomy Cafe Attic," at http://www.astron-omycafe.net/weird/weird.html

[46] Naomi Oreskes, "The Scientific Consensus on Climate Change," Science, 306: 5702, p. 1686, 3 December 2004.

[47] Benny Peiser (b.j.peiser@livjm.ac.uk), "100% Consensus! Science Publishes Soviet-Style Results On Climate Change", Cambridge Conference Network (CCNet ) (6 December 2004).

[48] "Remembering the R G I, The Railway Goan Institute, Nairobi Kenya: Timeline 1899 ~ 1967," http://www.goacom.com/culture/biographies/rgi/timeline.htm

[49] 2008 International Conference on Climate Change, New York City, Mar 2-4. Audio files available at www.Heartland.org

[50] "Dr. William Worrall Mayo and the Minnesota Territory" Mayo Clinic Proceedings at http://www.mayoclinicproceedings.com/inside.asp?AID=2542&UID=

[51] Rush Holt, "Trying to Get Us to Change Course," book and film review of Al Gore's An Inconvenient Truth, in Science, vol. 317, (13 July, 2007).

[52] H. Douglas Lightfoot, Nobody's Fuel: Energy supply is more important than climate change, (www.nobodysfuel.com).

[53] ABC News, "Global Warming Denier: Fraud or 'Realist'?: Physicist Says Humans Will Benefit From Warmer Planet," at http://abcnews.go.com/Technology/GlobalWarming/story?id=4506059&page=1

[54] CBS News, "Al Gore's New Campaign: Tells 60 Minutes That Doubting Global Warming Is Man-Made Is Akin To Believing Earth Is Flat http://www.cbsnews.com/stories/2008/03/27/60minutes/main3974389.shtml

[55] VPL Molecular Spectroscopic Database at http://vpl.astro.washington.edu/spectra/frontpage.htm

[56] See, for example, Steve Milloy, "This "global warming" thing... what Watt is what?," at http://www.junkscience.com/Greenhouse/What_Watt.html

[57] Ashley Phillips, "Poison Ivy Thrives With Climate Change: New Data Strengthens Global Warming's Connection to Weed Growth," ABC News at http://www.abcnews.go.com/Technology/story?id=3318396

[58] "Climate Change: A Heating Bill For The Planet," Speigel Online International Oct 31, 2006, at http://www.spiegel.de/international/0,1518,445651,00.html

[59] Annual Energy Review 2006 at Energy Information Agency at Department of Energy (www.eia.doe.gov). Go to

http://tonto.eia.doe.gov/bookshelf/SearchResults.asp?title=Annual+En ergy+Review to download pdf file.

[60] Linda Greenhouse "Justices Say E.P.A. Has Power to Act on Harmful Gases, *New York Times,* April 3, 2007.

[61] Roger Pielke, Tom Wigley, and Christopher Green, "Dangerous Assumptions," *Nature: Commentary*, vol. **452**, April 2008.

# Appendix

## *Abbreviations*

30 Myr Filter ................. 30-million year temperature average for each point
$CO_2$ ................................................................................Carbon dioxide
COPSE....A model for biochemical cycling in Antarctica, phanerozoic time
EIA ................................................................. Energy Information Agency
ESRL/GMD ......Earth System Res. Laboratory/Global Monitoring Division
GCM ................................................................. General Circulation Model
GEOCARB III ......A model for $CO_2$ over Antarctica over Phanerozoic time
GHG ............................................................................. Green House Gas
$H_2O$ ................................................................................................ Water
HIGWIGC .......Human-Induced-Global-Warming-Induced-Global-Cooling
IPCC ...................................... Inter*governmental* Panel on Climate Change
MJD .......................................................................... Modified Julian Day
MWP ....................................................................Medieval Warm Period
NCDC........................................................... National Climate Data Center
NESDIS ..... National Environmental Satellite Data and Information Service
NOAA ................ National Oceanographic and Atmospheric Administration
UNEP........................................... United Nations Environment Programme
VSMOW............................................... Vienna Standard Mean Ocean Water


## *$CO_2$ Production by Fuels*

With all the blather about "carbon footprints" and "carbon credits'" it is a good idea to have some solid numbers available, specifically those about $CO_2$ production by fossil fuels. The raw data provided by the Energy Information Agency [see latest —2006 — *Annual Energy Review* at ref. 59] tell us the annual amount of $CO_2$ (in millions of metric tons — tonnes) produced by each fuel, and the annual amount of energy produced by each fuel (in quads). I won't bother with leading you through the conversions to rational units, but there are some interesting results.

In 2005, the US produced 5,929 megatonnes (5.929 trillion kg) of $CO_2$ (1.62 trillion kg of carbon therein). We produced 89.36 EJ ($8.96 \times 10^{19}$ joules) of energy from fossil fuels, of which 23.75 EJ came from coal, 41.95

EJ from oil, and 23.66 EJ from natural gas. These three fuels produced 84.9 percent of our primary energy.

In terms of $CO_2$ produced per unit of energy, methane (the primary component of natural gas) is lowest, as expected. Petroleum produces 25% more $CO_2$ per unit energy, and coal produces 81% more $CO_2$, both compared to natural gas.

## Table 4: $CO_2$ per Unit Energy

| Fuel | $CO_2$ per unit energy (relative) |
|---|---|
| Natural Gas | 1.0 |
| Petroleum | 1.25 |
| Coal | 1.81 |

It is also of interest to express $CO_2$ production in terms of joules of energy produced per kilogram of $CO_2$ produced.

## Table 5: Megajoules per kilogram of $CO_2$ Produced

| Fuel | Megajoules of Energy per kilogram of $CO_2$ produced |
|---|---|
| Natural Gas | 20.1 |
| Petroleum | 16.0 |
| Coal | 11.1 |

## Energy Facts and Figures

### Table 6 : Energy Conversion Factors

| Multiply Number of ▼ | By ▼ to get joules |
|---|---|
| Watt-seconds | 1 |
| British Thermal Units (BTU) | 1 055.055 852 62 |
| Quadrillion BTUs (quads) | $1.055 \times 10^{18}$ |
| Kilowatt-hours (kWh) | $3.6 \times 10^6$ |
| Horsepower-hours | $2.69 \times 10^6$ |
| kilocalories (kcal) | 4186.8 |

| calories (cal) | 4.1868 |
|---|---|
| Therm (=$10^5$ BTU) | $1.055 \times 10^8$ |
| Foot-pound | 1.36 |
| Erg | $1 \times 10^{-7}$ |
| Watt-year | $3.16 \times 10^7$ |

## Metric Prefixes

Prefixes are useful abbreviations used in spoken and written prose. For example, we annually use about 105 000 000 000 000 000 000 joules in the US. While all those zeros are very important in calculations, we can abbreviate it by saying that we use about 105 exajoules (EJ) per year.

Note that all prefix abbreviations for numbers greater than one (except $k$ for *kilo*) are capitalized, while all prefix abbreviations for numbers less than one are lower-case. ("M" is not "m" and "P" is not "p", for example.) One Greek letter ($\mu$, "mu") is used for *micro* (millionth). Pharmacists use a double-letter prefix *mc* for *micro*. The capitalization rules apply to the abbreviations, but not to the words. For example our annual energy demand is about 105 EJ, or 105 exajoules. There are $10^{12}$ microphones in one megaphone.

## Table 7: Metric Prefixes

| E (exa) | $10^{18}$ | 1 000 000 000 000 000 000 |
|---|---|---|
| P (peta) | $10^{15}$ | 1 000 000 000 000 000 |
| T (tera) | $10^{12}$ | 1 000 000 000 000 |
| G (giga) | $10^{9}$ | 1 000 000 000 |
| M (mega) | $10^{6}$ | 1 000 000 |
| k (kilo) | $10^{3}$ | 1 000 |
| m (milli) | $10^{-3}$ | 0.001 |
| $\mu$ (micro)  mc | $10^{-6}$ | 0.000 001 |
| n (nano) | $10^{-9}$ | 0.000 000 001 |
| p (pico) | $10^{-12}$ | 0.000 000 000 001 |
| f (femto) | $10^{-15}$ | 0.000 000 000 000 001 |
| a (atto) | $10^{-18}$ | 0.000 000 000 000 000 001 |

# Our Energy Sources

## US Annual Energy Consumption

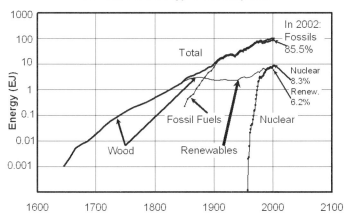

Figure 38: Sources of annual US energy consumption since about 1645. Note the logarithmic scale on the vertical axis; each horizontal line represents a factor of 10 from the next-lower one. Accordingly, it is hard to distinguish the recent total energy consumption from the fossil sources (coal, oil, and natural gas), which is 85.5% of the total. All US energy data in all graphs and tables come from www.eia.doe.

We humans are big consumers of energy. Figure 38 shows the historical energy usage in the US from 1645 to 2002. Until about 1850, wood provided virtually all the nation's energy. (We exclude any energy obtained from draft animals.) Since then, we have added hydropower, wood waste, municipal waste, geothermal power, wind power, and corn-based ethanol to wood to form a classification called *renewables*. At present, the renewables comprise about 6% of our energy usage. Nuclear fission provides about 8% of our energy.

The actual amounts of the energy consumption from various fuels varies, but the percentages remain nearly constant.

# Table 8:  U.S. Energy by the Numbers

## Overall Energy Consumption 2006

|  | Exajoules |
|---|---|
| Supply | 110.56 |
| Consumption | 105.36 |
| Fossil Fuels | 89.42 |
| Nuclear Energy | 8.66 |
| Hydro & Biomass | 6.51 |
| Geothermal | 0.37 |
| Wind | 0.27 |
| Solar | 0.07 |

## Electric power Sector

| Number of Power Generators (Total) | **13,834** |
|---|---|
| Utilities | 9,249 |
| Indep. Power Producers | 4,585 |
| Nameplate Capacity (MW) | **998,122** |
| Utilities | 610,057 |
| Indep. Power Producers | 388,066 |
| Retail Sales (million kWh) | **3,665,000** |
| Residential | 1,354,000 |
| Commercial | 1,301,000 |
| Industrial | 1,002,000 |

## Electricity Sources (million kWh)

| Conventional | **3,993,000** |
|---|---|
| Coal | 1,987,000 |
| Natural gas | 808,000 |
| Nuclear | 787,000 |
| Hydropower | 288,000 |
| Petroleum | 93,200 |
| Biomass | 55,600 |
| Renewable | **41,100** |
| Geothermal | 14,800 |
| Wind | 25,800 |
| Solar & PV | 500 |

All Energy                              Electrical Energy

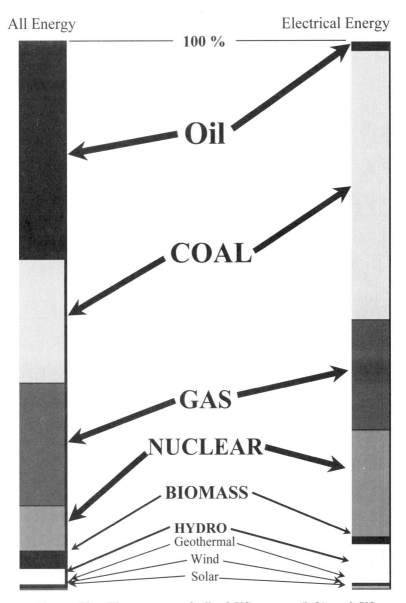

100 %

Oil

COAL

GAS

NUCLEAR

BIOMASS

HYDRO
Geothermal
Wind
Solar

**Figure 39: The sources of all of US energy (left) and US electrical energy (right) for 2006. The top line represents 100%.**

Figure 40 shows the sources of U.S. energy in 2004, as percentages from coal, oil, and natural gas (lumped together as Fossil Fuels), Nuclear, and Renewable (which includes all renewable sources, but consists almost exclusively of biomass and hydro).

Figure 41 shows a further breakdown into categories. For example, coal provides 45% of our fossil-fuel energy. The right-hand graph of Fig. 41 shows where our renewable energy comes from — primarily hydropower and biomass (which is mostly wood and wood waste). Solar and wind provide a mere 3% of our renewable energy, and a mere one-sixth of one percent of our total energy.

## Energy Consumption 2004

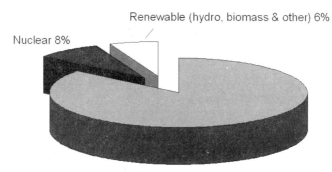

Figure 40: Present (2004) sources of energy in the US. Note that fossil fuels provide 86% of our energy, and that nuclear fission provides 8%. Renewables provide 6%, but the overwhelming amount of that energy comes from biomass (primarily wood and wood waste) and hydropower.

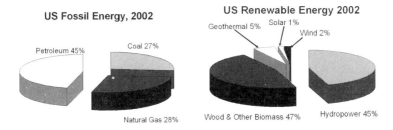

US Fossil Energy, 2002

Petroleum 45%

Coal 27%

Natural Gas 28%

US Renewable Energy 2002

Geothermal 5%  Solar 1%

Wind 2%

Wood & Other Biomass 47%    Hydropower 45%

**Figure 41: The sources of our fossil energy (left) and of our renewable energy (right).** Note that solar and wind *together* produce only 3% of our *renewable* energy, and one-sixth of one percent of our total energy consumption.

Table 9 shows annual US energy consumption for 2002 and 2005, with translations to year-round average power consumption. It also shows our electrical power consumption as a separate item.

## Table 9: US Energy at a Glance

| Misc | 2002 | 2005 |
|---|---|---|
| US Energy | 102.8 EJ | 105.4 EJ |
| US Power (all) | 3 253.2 GW | 3 335.4 GW |
| US Elec Power | 440.0 GW | 461.9 GW |

# *Our Energy "Sinks"*

Where does all that energy go? Just as the sources are varied, so are the "sinks," the places we use energy. Fig. 42 shows that transportation gobbles up 27% of the energy, industries 33%, residences 22%, and commercial establishments 18%.

# *Electricity*

Electricity is playing an ever-increasing role in the energy picture; however it is not a *source* of energy. It is a *carrier* of energy. Some 40.9% of our energy goes into the production of electricity. Because most electricity is produced by heat engines (steam engines, gas turbines, diesel engines ...), there are very large "conversion losses" in converting heat to work.

## US Energy Use by Sector, 2002

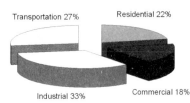

Transportation 27%    Residential 22%

Industrial 33%    Commercial 18%

## US Non-Electric Energy 2002

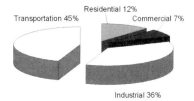

Residential 12%

Transportation 45%    Commercial 7%

Industrial 36%

**Figure 42: (Left). Energy consumption by sector. About a third of our energy goes into industry, and a quarter into transportation. (Right). Energy use by sector, but with electricity left out of the picture. Note that commercial establishments use only 7% of the energy (probably by burning natural gas), but when electrical energy is included (left), commercial establishments use 18% of our energy.**

The system-average efficiency of producing electricity from such devices is 34.8%. Some of the produced electricity is used in the power plants themselves, and there are transmission and distribution losses amounting to 9% of the generated electricity. Consumers wind up using electrical energy that is 31.1% of the heat energy required to produce it.

Figure 42 (right) shows our energy consumption exclusive of electricity. In other words, it includes only fuel used on-site.

Because of its versatility, electricity has steadily risen in prominence. In 1949 (see Fig. 43), we used about 14% of our energy to produce electricity, but we now use 41%. Although Fig. 43 shows the fraction tending toward a saturation limit of perhaps 45%, there is every possibility that a strong demand will cause further increase.

Specifically, if the automotive industry develops a battery that will make electric cars practical, demand for electricity will certainly rise, and demand for motor fuels will either fall or rise less rapidly. In any event, electrical energy as a fraction of total energy will rise.

About half of the energy used to produce our electricity comes from coal (see Fig. 44). Nuclear fission and natural gas each contribute roughly 20% of our electricity. Oil contributes a mere 3%.

Geothermal, wood, and wood waste contribute about 2.1% of our electricity.

## Energy Used to Produce Electricity

Figure 43: The fraction of our total energy used for the production of electricity, 1949 to present. Starting from about 14% in 1949, the fraction has steadily risen to 41% at the present time. Presently, we use about 105 EJ for all purposes, including 40.9 EJ of that to produce electricity.

# Electrical Energy by Source

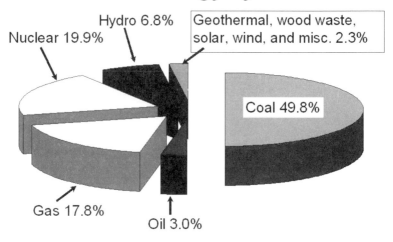

Figure 44: The sources of our electricity. About half comes from coal, one-fifth each from nuclear fission and natural gas, and one-fifteenth from hydro. The non-hydro renewables produce only 2.3% of our electricity.

# Do you subscribe to
# THE ENERGY ADVOCATE?

THE ENERGY ADVOCATE is a monthly energy newsletter that has celebrated it twelfth year of publication. We receive no support from any industry of any kind, and do not accept handouts from the government either. Furthermore, we carry no advertising.

We are beholden only to our subscribers. They want unvarnished truth.

For a sample, write to The Energy Advocate, P.O. Box 7609, Pueblo West, CO 81007 or to corkhayden@comcast.net. You can also send a fax to (719) 547-7819

# And have you read *The Solar Fraud: Why Solar Energy Won't Run the World*?

Howard C. Hayden presents the complete solar energy picture, including all manifestations, and shows how a fully implemented solar program could not provide enough energy to run a civilized world.

The book, now in the second edition, is available at The Energy Advocate, P.O. Box 7609, Pueblo West, CO 81007, or at www.energyadvocate.com.